Posing Open-Ended Questions

in the primary math classroom

Christina Myren

Dear Myriam,
Thank you for your friendship
and support. May all your
problems have multiple solutions.
Fondly,
Christina

Math
Perspectives
Teacher Development Center

Published by
Math Perspectives Teacher Development Center
PO Box 29418
Bellingham, WA 98228
www.mathperspectives.com

Copyright © 2013 by Christina Myren

Distributed by
Didax, Inc.
395 Main Street
Rowley, MA 01969-1207
(800) 458-0024
www.didax.com

A B C D E 17 16 15 14 13

ISBN 978-0-9848381-2-7

Editor: Teacher Development Center
Cover Design: Ken Harris II
Production Coordinator: JoEllen Key

Printed in the United States of America with soy based inks on recycled, acid-free paper

*This book is dedicated
to the memory of my mother,
Myrtle Iverson,
who was an inspiration
to the teaching profession.*

Special thanks to:

My sister Heidi Thomas and my friend Jane Traut, who shared their insights about posing open-ended questions with kindergartners.

Jan Goodman, my editor, and the staff at Teaching Resource Center

The children at Acacia Elementary, Park Oaks Elementary, and Walnut Elementary in Thousand Oaks, California whose work is reproduced in this book.

Janet Trentacosta, Jaine Kopp, Elisabeth Javor, Fran Threewit and the members of the editorial panel for California Mathematics Council's magazine, *The ComMuniCator*. Many of the ideas in this book first appeared in that magazine.

Contents

Book-at-a-Glance

This book is a collection of fifteen open-ended math questions for kindergarten, first and second grade children. The questions in this book deal with animals, birthdays, mittens, and other topics that capture the interest of young children.

The problems are open-ended because they have multiple solutions and/or multiple approaches to reach one solution. Appropriate children's literature serves as a springboard for many of the lessons. Classroom examples of typical student responses at each grade level are shown and discussed to provide teachers with possible assessment tools.

The problems are intentionally designed to cover a three-grade span. It is often quite valuable to repeat questions (or present them with minor modifications) throughout the school year and at various grade levels. As students revisit a problem, teachers will gain insights into student growth over time. Each lesson contains the following:

Overview

This is a short synopsis of the lesson that includes a summary of the activity and an approximate time frame.

Materials

Materials necessary for the lesson are listed. These include teacher supplies as well as student supplies. Some items may be marked optional.

Description

This is the "how-to" part of the lesson. Step-by-step details are provided to help teachers implement the lesson in their classrooms. Modifications for particular grade levels are included, when appropriate.

Student Responses and Assessment

A range of student responses is included with each lesson. The responses represent a culturally, linguistically and socio-economically diverse group of children who have actually participated in the lessons across the grade levels. All lessons contain a continuum of **levels of understanding** to offer the teacher tools to evaluate student responses. This section often features questions that the teacher can use when observing children at work and writing anecdotal comments. Suggestions for similar open-ended problems or extensions are also included.

References

Literature selections or related articles are listed in the reference section at the end of each lesson.

"If we allowed children to show us what they can do rather than accepting what they usually do, we would be in for some grand surprises. As adults, our feeble expectations of children's capabilities puts brakes on their potential."

Mem Fox, *Radical Reflections*

Posing Open-Ended Questions in the Primary Math Classroom

Who has the "answers" in primary grade math classrooms? Children learn at an early age to look for answers from the adults in their lives, rather than from within themselves. In many primary classrooms, young children spend the majority of their time learning that there is one right answer in math; the teacher knows it; and their goal is to find it. Children are rarely asked to describe the strategies that led them to their solution, nor are they asked to examine other possible "right" answers. In fact, when a teacher asks a young child how she has arrived at an answer, the child's first instinct may be to get an eraser because she assumes that she is wrong.

The assumption that grown-ups have all the answers creates a hardship for both children and teachers. Children become one-dimensional in their thinking and are denied the opportunity to become mathematically powerful problem-solvers. Teachers develop a limited view of their students' mathematical progress and are deprived of tools to evaluate the effectiveness of their instructional program.

This is why it is essential that we pose open-ended questions in all math classrooms, beginning in the primary grades. In the process of responding to open-ended questions, children:
- learn to look to themselves for answers and to value themselves as problem solvers;
- build respect for diverse solutions while learning multiple ways of answering questions; and
- develop and express mathematical power.

As students respond to open-ended questions, teachers gain valuable information about each child's:
- ability to think mathematically;
- ease with mathematical communication, orally, pictorially and in writing;
- problem-solving strategies; and
- ability to consider multiple viewpoints and approaches in problem-solving

In addition, student responses provide teachers with insights about their program:
- the overall effectiveness of their math curriculum;
- whether specific lesson objectives have been achieved;
- the appropriateness of the task and the instructional strategies used; and
- whether to modify and/or extend the lesson in the future.

How do teachers encourage children to communicate mathematically? Given that students may be unaccustomed to exploring open-ended questions, it is the teacher's responsibility to create a climate where children are encouraged to share their ideas about mathematics. This task requires risk taking on the part of both adults and children. Teachers need to feel confident that children have the ability to solve their own problems, in a supportive, trusting atmosphere. Children must learn to trust themselves; know that mistakes are a part of the learning process; and recognize that persistence is necessary in order to become powerful mathematicians.

The *NCTM Curriculum and Evaluation Standards for School Mathematics* validates this view:

> *"Ideally, children should share their thinking with other children and with teachers, and they should learn several ways for representing problems and strategies for solving them. In addition, they should learn to value the process of solving the problems as much as they value the solutions."*

To foster a climate conducive to open-ended problem solving, the classroom must encourage risk taking and divergent thinking. Open-ended questions will be most successful in classrooms where:

- Children are encouraged to see themselves as problem solvers, independent of the teacher or textbook.
- Questions are NOT answered immediately by the teacher; rather, children share a variety of approaches and solutions.
- Teachers provide ample time for children to grapple with questions and formulate solutions.
- Teachers model a variety of communication tools —drawings, diagrams, graphs, tables, and oral dictation, as well as written work.
- Support is provided for students to develop mathematical language, through word banks, student-created dictionaries and ample time for discussion.
- Children solve mathematical problems in real-life situations throughout the curriculum, in all subject areas.

It is a challenge to help students communicate mathematically. Initially, when we ask children to explain their answers, they may be intimidated. Many young children think there might be something wrong with their answer. Teachers need to listen carefully to children as they answer these tough questions, and encourage them to be persistent and to look to themselves for solutions. Once young children see themselves as problem solvers, they will take delight in drawing and "writing" about their ideas. Older elementary children can often be resistant to writing in math class because they have never done it before. Younger children, however, have no preconceived notions about what mathematics should be, and enjoy expressing their ideas on paper.

What should teachers expect from student responses to open-ended questions? Expect that your students will respond on many different levels to the lessons in this book. Children bring a wealth of prior knowledge and a natural curiosity to the mathematics classroom, but they vary greatly in their ability to utilize and express this information. The teacher's responsibility is to help each child move forward, to grow in his or her ability to understand and express the concepts that connect to each open-ended question.

It is important to remember that it takes time for students to gain fluency in the language of mathematics. Children need to revisit open-ended math problems throughout the year and in successive years, so that they can develop new insights and approaches to a particular situation.

Recognize that real learning is gradual and often happens imperceptibly. Teachers rarely expect children to master an idea or concept when it is first introduced. The same should hold true as children begin to communicate in mathematics. While revisiting lessons and concepts, thoughtful probing and questioning of students' ideas will gently nudge them to higher levels of understanding. Children need time and multiple opportunities to grapple with, and then embrace, a concept as their own.

Finally, teachers should expect to be delighted and surprised with student responses to open-ended questions. After an initial level of comfort is achieved, students will look forward to solving the problems, sharing their ideas, revising their work and eventually, generating new questions for the class to explore. Teachers will likely discover that there is much joy and excitement in our role as facilitators, as we guide our students to develop true mathematical power.

References

Fox, Mem. *Radical Reflections*. New York: Houghton Mifflin Harcourt, 2001.

National Council of Teachers of Mathematics. *Curriculum and Evaluation Standards for School Mathematics.* Reston, Virginia: NCTM, 1989.

Creating an Open-Ended Math Environment

This section gives you an overview of what you might see in a primary classroom where students are engaged with open-ended problems. It discusses the physical set-up, necessary materials, and the role of children and teachers.

What is the physical set-up of the classroom?
First, there should be a place in your classroom for the children to share with the class the discoveries they have made. Preferably, the whole class can sit in this area close enough to hear and see their classmates' work. A carpeted area is nice, but not required. If available, an overhead projector and screen can be used to highlight students' work so that all children can see it. If the children are sitting close together, however, the actual children's work can be viewed by the class without an overhead projector. Individual chalkboards, chalk, and erasers will enhance whole class discussion, when appropriate.

What materials are necessary? Children should have easy access to a range of mathematics manipulatives so that they can explore and represent solutions concretely. These materials should be in labeled containers on low shelves that are also labeled for easy clean-up and return.

The following is a list of the most common classroom math materials necessary to solve these problems:
- unifix cubes or other linking cubes
- pattern blocks or other similar geometric materials
- counting materials such as wooden cubes, tiles, and so on
- junk or treasure boxes
- geoboards

Other materials for specific lessons are listed at the beginning of each lesson. There are also classroom supplies that should be easily accessible to all the children and the teacher:

Children's Supplies
- unlined 8½" by 11" paper
- lined writing paper
- pencils
- crayons
- scissors
- glue or gluesticks
- staplers
- individual chalkboards, chalk and erasers*

Teacher's Supplies
- chart paper
- marking pens
- post-it notes
- overhead transparencies *
- overhead projector *
- screen *

* These supplies are optional.

What should the teacher see as children solve open-ended questions? The classroom should be alive with children thoroughly engaged in their work. Expect noise and clutter as the children delve into these problems. Some children might work alone, while others work with one or more partners. Primary grade children often work best in groups of two, but if the children choose to work in larger groups, allow them to do so. If larger groups are formed, make sure that the children work productively together. Most often, the children are grouped randomly by the teacher. This precludes hurt feelings for the child that seems to always be the last one chosen.

The children choose their work area. Some children prefer to work at tables or desks, while others enjoy working on the floor. The children who work on the floor often choose the individual chalkboards as a backing for their paper as they write.

When the children are thoroughly engrossed in their work, it may be necessary to extend the time. For children to be successful problem solvers, you may need to be flexible with the day's schedule. When most of the class has finished, begin to discuss the task.

What is the role of the classroom teacher? The role of the teacher is two-fold. First, you need to be sure that the problem is thoroughly understood by the children. This does not mean that you teach specific problem-solving strategies; rather, that you check for understanding. You can ask students to re-state the problem in their own words, brainstorm approaches to solve it, and raise questions to clarify the problem. To assure that the problem is accessible to all students, you may wish to present it in a variety of learning modalities—visually, orally and kinesthetically (through dramatic play, modeling).

After the problem is understood, the teacher becomes a facilitator. As the children work, you can circulate around the room to observe children as they solve the problem. You will gain information about children's diverse approaches to problem-solving as well as their ability to work individually or in groups. When children ask questions, you might answer them with another question or redirect the question to the partners or the entire class.

The teacher is also a facilitator during whole class discussions which can occur anytime during the lesson. It is crucial to provide time for discussion after children have completed their work, to allow them to share their strategies and thoughts about the problem. The children explore and talk about mathematical ideas during this time, while the teacher uses questioning techniques to probe and prod the children's thinking to higher levels of understanding.

Overview of The Lessons

Fifteen open-ended problems and additional extensions are described in this book. Each problem addresses the needs of kindergarten, first, and second grade children, and has examples of student work from each grade level.

The following is a list of the fifteen problems and their relationship to the various concepts/strands of mathematics:

Lesson Title	Overview	Concepts & Strands	Literature Connection
1 Eggs & Chicks	Children compare the total number of Mrs. Sato's eggs to the total number of baby chicks that hatch.	Number Logic & Language	*Mrs. Sato's Hens* by Laura Min
2 How Many Snails?	Children count and sort objects and identify their attributes.	Number Logic & Language Sorting & Classifying	*How Many Snails?* by Paul Giganti, Jr.
3 How Many Wheels?	Children use their knowledge of wheels on bicycles and cars to find out how many wheels take children home from a party.	Logic & Language Number	*10 For Dinner* by Jo Ellen Bogart
4 What Fits Inside the Mitten?	Children arrange objects by size and determine how many objects will fit in a mitten.	Measurement Sequencing	*The Mitten* by Jan Brett
5 Crazy Mixed-Up Animals	Children explore how many animals they can make by mixing up the heads and bodies of animals.	Discrete Math (combinations) Logic & Language Patterns	*All Mixed Up* by Kees Moerbeek
6 Safari Toss/ Color Toss	Children collect data from rolling a die and then interpret the results.	Statistics & Probability Discrete Math Number Data Representation	none
7 Birthday Candles	Children explore whether there are enough candles for upcoming family birthdays.	Number Logic & Language	none

Lesson Title	Overview	Concepts & Strands	Literature Connection
8 Sylvester's Pebbles	Children sort and count rocks in three or more ways.	Sorting Data Representation	*Sylvester & the Magic Pebble* by William Steig -or- *Everybody Needs A Rock* by Byrd Baylor
9 The Duckling Problem	Children create stories and/or number sentences about what would happen if the Mallard's ducklings wander away.	Create-a-Problem Representing Numbers Subtraction Addition	*Make Way For Ducklings* by Robert McCloskey
10 Pattern Block Puzzles	Children use geometric materials to create and solve riddles and puzzles.	Geometry Logic & Language	*Shapes, Shapes, Shapes* by Tana Hoban
11 Unifix Trains	Children find possible combinations of three or four different colored cars for a train.	Discrete Math (combinations) Patterns	*Freight Train* by Donald Crews
12 Measuring Neil's Desk	Children explore what happens when they measure a desk with objects of various sizes.	Measurement Number Comparing	*The Line Up Book* by Marisabina Russo
13 Read-a-Graph	Children interpret data from a graph.	Statistics Logic & Language	none
14 Geoboard Geometry	Children create pictures or designs on a geoboard and describe what they've made.	Spatial Sense Geometry Logic & Language	none
15 Sweet Treats	Children create their own math investigations using snack-sized bags of candies.	Logic Data Representation Number	*The M&M's Counting Book* by Barbara Barbieri McGrath

Eggs and Chicks

Materials

- Unifix cubes, wooden cubes, or other counting materials
- *Mrs. Sato's Hens* by Laura Min
- Plastic or paper eggs as counters (optional)
- Unlined paper
- Pencils, crayons, and/or colored marking pens
- Overhead projector (optional)
- Screen (optional)
- Overhead transparencies of children's work (optional)
- Post-it notes (optional)

Overview

This lesson can be a good place for you and the children to begin because it focuses on an area of mathematics in which students and teachers are usually most comfortable — Number. If Mrs. Sato and her friend found two eggs on Monday, three eggs on Tuesday, four eggs on Wednesday, five eggs on Thursday, and six eggs on Friday, how many eggs did they find? First and second grade children are asked to find the total number of eggs and decide if all the eggs hatched at the end of the story, while kindergarten children simply find the total number of eggs. Allow at least 40 minutes for the children to hear the story and solve the problem.

Description

The springboard for this problem is the book *Mrs. Sato's Hens* by Laura Min. In this story, a young girl visits Mrs. Sato and helps count her eggs. On Monday they counted two white eggs, on Tuesday they counted three brown eggs, on Wednesday they counted four speckled eggs, on Thursday they counted five small eggs, and on Friday they counted six big eggs. Finally on Saturday they didn't count any eggs and the picture shows Mrs. Sato and her friend surrounded by baby chicks.

Gather the children around you as you read the story to the class twice. Count together the number of chicks that are shown on the last page. There are fifteen. Have the children retell the facts of the story as you write the following numbers and problem on the chalkboard:

> 2 white eggs
> 3 brown eggs
> 4 speckled eggs
> 5 small eggs
> 6 big eggs
> 15 chicks

Did all the chicks hatch? Show and tell how you solved this problem.

Discuss the problem and give the children the opportunity to clarify the question. Explain that they can use any of the materials in the classroom to find out if all the chicks hatched. You may want to have paper or plastic eggs for them to count. Give them blank paper to record (using pictures and/or words) their answers so they can report back to the class at a later time. Tell them they may work alone or with a partner, but each child needs to prepare his or her own "report."

As the children work, circulate throughout the room observing them. Use this time to encourage those children who stay on task and to refocus those who need it. Designate a place for them to put their finished work and a task for them to do when the work is complete. When all the children have finished, remind them that they will get a chance to share their reports later.

Sometime before the next part of this lesson, look through the children's work for samples you can make into overhead transparencies. Choose the samples of work that are obviously on the right track and/or have a unique way of approaching the problem. Ask the children whose work you chose if they are willing to explain their solution(s) to the rest of the class.

Finally, have the class gather together around the overhead projector and ask the children to share their work. Be sure to emphasize the positive aspects of each child's report and have the child explain his or her thinking. Discuss the samples and provide the opportunity for the children to revise their work based on the information gained from the samples that were shared.

In kindergarten, the lesson would be similar, but without the expectation of writing about the answer. Children may choose to record what they find out by drawing a picture, and the teacher or another adult can take dictation on post-it notes or the back of the picture about the child's thinking. Read the story initially in a large group. Then reread the story and have the children work on the problem in small groups. Counting materials such as plastic eggs, unifix cubes, or paper eggs would be helpful for K's. Expect that the task of counting the eggs to twenty will be a difficult one for many kindergarten children, especially if you choose to do this task during the first half of the school year.

Student Responses and Assessment

In responding to this problem, some children chose to represent the eggs by drawing. Some used unifix cubes or pattern blocks, while others made tally marks. Reports also varied — some children simply drew their answer, others used words and pictures, and a few children only wrote about their solutions.

The samples shown are from the first month of school in a kindergarten class and a combination first and second grade class. The results might be much more sophisticated from either class later in the year, yet both teachers considered the lesson a success. It is a problem that all the children felt comfortable attempting to solve. The discussion after the children completed their responses gave the class additional information, and the children in both classes were allowed to change their responses based on the information.

Small motor development in young children varies tremendously from child to child. Some children may have marvelous ideas about how to solve a problem, but very little skill at putting those ideas down on paper. There are several ways to record children's ideas other than having them always draw or write about the solution. Consider doing some of the following as your children work on this and other open-ended problems:

- Take anecdotal records as the children work, either using post-it notes on a clipboard to later attach to the child's work or actually writing on the back of the child's paper.

- Have a camera ready to take pictures of the children at work as they solve the problem.

- Use a tape recorder to have children elaborate on their written report, either as they share with the class or individually.

- Videotape the children as they are working and as they share.

In the classroom, expect the responses to vary. Most kindergartners, and some first graders will find just keeping track of the twenty eggs to be a challenging task. Kindergarten children, if this is their first experience solving a problem of this nature, may focus on other aspects of the story rather than the number of eggs. It might be helpful to consider **levels of understanding** that children have when answering this question. These are (from the most basic to the fullest grasp of understanding):

Levels of Understanding

▼	▼	▼	▼	▼
The child demonstrates a simple understanding of the story with no reference to mathematics.	The child depicts some of the basic mathematical elements of the problem.	The child depicts most of the mathematical elements of the problem.	The child demonstrates knowledge of more or less in relation to the eggs and chicks.	The child demonstrates knowledge of more or less in relation to the eggs and chicks and uses the number five to express the difference.

Consider these levels as we look at some student work.

Kacey, a kindergarten child, demonstrates a simple understanding of the story with no reference to the mathematics. In her work, she carefully drew and told about the story without mentioning the number of eggs. She dictated to her teacher: "The chicken was crying because he thought Mrs. Sato was going to take the eggs. She wanted the eggs to hatch." As with many students new to this problem-solving process, Kacey was enthralled with the story and paid little attention to the math she was asked to do. Some students this age, like Kacey, find it hard to hold both the story and the problem in mind at the same time.

In the same kindergarten class, however, many children were able to tell there were twenty eggs in all, and some even tried to compare this with number of chicks that hatched. Both Lydia and Alan attempted to explain what happened to the eggs that did not hatch.

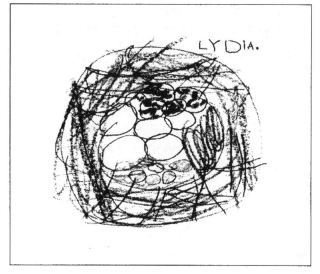

Lydia depicted most of the basic mathematical elements of the problem, but did not draw all the eggs or state the total number of eggs. She drew only 15 eggs, but said that there were more eggs than chickens: "The four speckled eggs, the five little eggs, the white big eggs. There were more eggs than chickens. Maybe they were eating eggs."

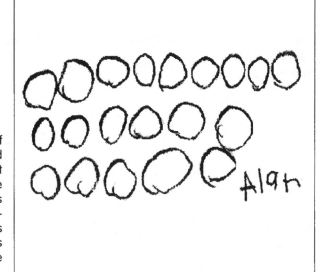

Alan demonstrated knowledge of "less" in relation to the eggs and chicks by implication, but did not give the exact difference. He showed the total number of eggs in his drawing and knew the number of chicks. Alan dictated to his teacher: "There was twenty eggs and only fifteen chicks. I think the other eggs rolled away."

In first and second grade, also expect a variety of ways of looking at the problem.

Sammy, a first grader, demonstrated a simple understanding of the story with no reference to mathematics. His level of understanding was basic, even though his teacher gently prodded him about the number of eggs while he was working.

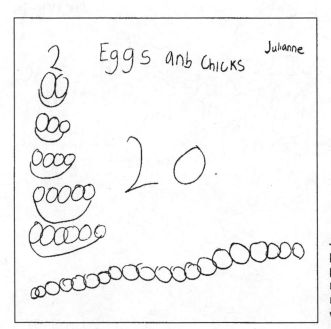

Julianne, another first grader, depicted some of the elements of the problem. She was able to tell the number of eggs, but did not elaborate on the number of the chicks when she shared with the class.

Gia, a first grader, depicted most of the mathematical elements of the problem. She drew and counted the correct number of eggs, and even stated that only 15 hatched.

Michael, while sharing his work with the class, demonstrated his knowledge about the difference between the chicks and eggs when he said he felt all the eggs hatched later, even though only 15 hatched at the end of the book. His sharing enhanced our understanding of Michael's view of the problem. In his writing and his sharing, no mention was made of the difference between the number of eggs and the number of chicks.

Both Mayra and Megan demonstrated a knowledge of more or less in relation to eggs and chicks and used the number five to express the difference.

Megan illustrated the chicks and the five unhatched eggs. Note that her picture contains an extra chick, but her writing says, "15 haht."

Mayra included an equation and drew each kind of egg.

Because both of these second grade children were able to find the difference between the two amounts, they demonstrated a high level of understanding of the mathematics in this problem.

▲▼▲

If we were to plot the children on a horizontal continuum according to their **levels of understanding** for this problem, it might look like this:

Levels of Understanding

Kacey Sammy ▼	Julianne ▼	Gia Lydia ▼	Michael Alan ▼	Megan Mayra ▼
The child demonstrates a simple understanding of the story with no reference to mathematics.	The child depicts some of the basic mathematical elements of the problem.	The child depicts most of the mathematical elements of the problem.	The child demonstrates knowledge of more or less in relation to the eggs and chicks.	The child demonstrates knowledge of more or less in relation to the eggs and chicks and uses the number five to express the difference.

If this is a first experience at solving problems like this, keep in mind that children who are not comfortable initially need more experiences of this type before we can assess them accurately. Trust that children will become better problem-solvers as their experiences with these open-ended problems increase. Your goal should be to move each child to higher levels of mathematical understanding throughout the year. Young children need many opportunities to grapple with open-ended problems to make the mathematics become real for them.

Extensions

A similar problem to try uses the book *Too Many Eggs* by Christine Butler. In this book, Mrs. Bear puts too many eggs in a birthday cake that calls for only six eggs. The problem would be:

> **Mrs. Bear first used five eggs, then added six eggs and finally added nine eggs to her cake batter. The recipe called for six eggs. How many extra eggs did she add?**

Both these problems, but especially the one about *Mrs. Sato's Hens*, would fit nicely in an integrated math/science unit on oviparous animals. Hatching eggs in the classroom would be the perfect opportunity to see if, in real-life, all the eggs do hatch.

References

Butler, M. Christine. *Too Many Eggs*. Boston: David R. Godine, 1988.

Min, Laura. *Mrs. Sato's Hens*. St. Paul, MN: Globe Publishing, 2000.

How Many Snails?

Materials

- Junk or treasure boxes, each containing a separate collection of buttons, bread tags, bottle caps, keys, etc.
- *How Many Snails?* by Paul Giganti, Jr., or one of the other books listed in the references
- Ten to twelve books from the classroom
- Unlined paper
- Pencils, crayons, and/or colored marking pens
- Overhead projector (optional)
- Screen (optional)
- Overhead transparencies of children's work (optional)
- Post-it notes (optional)

Overview

This activity spans three or four days. Children are asked to count and sort a group of materials. Although this is a rather directed lesson, it is one where children pose and answer their own questions. The lessons are based on the format of the book *How Many Snails?*

Description

Children are most successful at working cooperatively when the activity they are asked to do has been thoroughly modeled for them over time. They need to see the activity being done for two or three days before they are asked to work with a partner. This modeling reinforces the process of working together and also gives the children a chance to understand what is expected when they are asked to duplicate the game or activity on their own. The following series of lessons illustrates this process.

On the first day, read the book *How Many Snails?* to the children. This book, beautifully illustrated by Donald Crews, asks the children to first count an entire group of objects, then count them again in decreasingly smaller groups. For instance, one page has pictures of snails with the words, **"I wondered how many snails there were? How many had striped shells? How many had striped shells and stuck their heads out?"** Another page has pictures of flowers and reads, **"I wondered how many flowers there were? How many flowers were yellow? How many flowers were yellow with black centers?"**

After reading the book, ask the children to sit in a circle. Spread out a collection of books in the center. Make sure there is a variety of books. Ask the children, "What do you notice about these books?" Listen carefully as the children share their answers. You may want to list the attributes the children share on the chalkboard. Expect such characteristics as: big, little, paperback, hardback, real people, animal characters, pictures, no pictures, and other similar responses.

Model how to ask questions in the format of the book by saying. **"I wonder how many books there are? How many are paperback? How many are paperback and have animal stories?"** After the children have answered each of these questions, tell them, "I am going to ask three more questions. Listen to the questions and see if you can tell where I am getting the pattern for these questions." Then ask, **"I wonder how many books there are? How many are big? How many are big and have real stories?"** Discuss with the children the format of the questions along with their answers.

On the second day, begin by rereading the book *How Many Snails?* Then repeat the previous day's lesson using children from the class instead of books. Have 8 to 10 volunteers stand in front of the classroom. Ask the class, "What do you notice about these children?" List the attributes on the chalkboard. Continue by asking questions about the children. Begin with, **"I wonder how many children there are?"** Next ask, **"How many children are wearing short-sleeved shirts?"** and finally ask, **"How many children are wearing short-sleeved shirts and have long hair?"** This time when you talk about the format of the questions, see if the children can generate their own questions.

On the third day, choose two children to demonstrate the process of working together. Have the class sit in a circle with the two children in the middle. Ask the pair to take 15 to 20 items out of the junk box. Then ask them to talk about what they see. They should describe to each other (and the class) the characteristics of the items from the junk box. Next help the pair of children ask each other the three questions that have been modeled on the previous days:

- I wonder how many _____ there are?
- How many _____ are _____ ?
- How many _____ are _____ and have _____ ?

Sometimes it is helpful to write these questions on the chalkboard for the class to see. Make sure that each partner gets a chance to ask the questions. If time and interest permits, choose two more children to model the process.

Finally on the fourth day, have enough junk boxes or material ready so that each pair of children can take 15 to 20 items. Again, have a pair of children model the process for the rest of the class. Have the children work on this task in

partners. Because this task has been so thoroughly modeled, the children should be able to get right to work and ask questions about the materials and discuss their answers.

For older children, extend the task by having them work in partners or alone to write and illustrate their own pages for a class book. If you are unable to get a copy of Giganti's book, there are other books that would help children identify attributes for sorting. You could still use the format with these books, but you would not be able to refer back to *How Many Snails?* for the questions. These additional books are noted in the references.

Student Responses and Assessment:

Kindergarten children respond best to this activity orally and in small groups. One kindergarten teacher felt that this was such a valuable experience for her children that she planned to use different materials and do this activity several times throughout the year. Initially, in October, her children focused on the total number of items and only a few of the children were able to narrow the groups into smaller categories. The second time she tried this activity, in January, the children were able to find decreasingly smaller groups with much more ease. As the children matured, she felt they were more able understand that an object can simultaneously have two or more attributes. In January, many children were able to work in pairs to complete the lesson within the small group structure. No recording was asked of the children.

Another kindergarten teacher worked with the whole class to introduce this book and format. After she went through the whole group introductory lessons, she had each child make a snowman and decorate it. Each child then put his or her snowman on the floor as the class gathered around to ask questions about them. Working together, the children generated such questions as, "How many snowmen are there? How many are wearing scarves? How many are wearing scarves that are red?"

As the children worked to ask the questions in the format that was modeled, the kindergarten teachers found the following questions helpful in assessing their progress. She listened carefully as the children worked with one another to find out:

• How does the child work with a partner?

• Is the child able to verbalize several characteristics of the items being counted?

• Do the children use manipulatives to help solve the problem?

• Can the children explain to each other orally their thoughts about the problem?

• Can the children express themselves clearly by either drawing or writing about the solution? (for first and second grade, or at the very end of kindergarten).

• Does the child have a unique way of looking at or expressing the characteristics of the items being counted?

In first and second grade classrooms, group the children randomly for this activity. Primary grade children often work best in partners rather than larger groups. Some children may feel most comfortable working alone when it comes to making a page for the class book.

In looking at the written work of the children in first and second grade, the **levels of understanding** (from the most basic to the fullest grasp of understanding) for this lesson are:

Levels of Understanding

| The child depicts some of the items and asks or attempts to ask a question about the total number. | The child depicts the items and asks one or more questions which do not follow the pattern in the book. | The child depicts the items and poses questions that begin to follow the pattern in the book. | The child depicts the items and poses three questions that completely follow the pattern in the book. |

These same levels were seen by the kindergarten teachers as they observed their children respond to this activity orally. In their writing and drawing, first and second grade students showed a variety of responses to this problem.

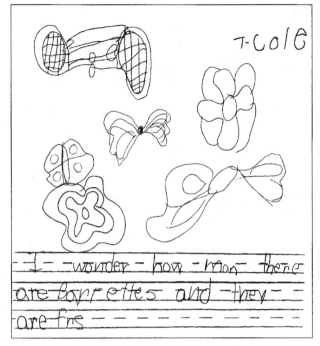

T-Cole was at the most basic level of understanding, as evidenced by her picture and one question about the number of barrettes that are flowered. She painstakingly drew the barrettes, but then hurried through her writing. When the teacher asked her about the format of her questions, she said she was finished.

Gia writes about animal barrettes, but she is on the next level of understanding. She included a question about the total number of barrettes and also asked about a subset of the total. Note how carefully Gia has drawn each animal barrette.

Both Cam and Leah are at the third level. They both asked about the total number and asked two more unrelated questions about the items being pictured.

Leah wrote about people. Her questions were: "I wonder how many children there are? How many boots are they wearing? How many children are little and have friends?"

Cam wrote about bones and asked, "I wonder how many there are big? How many bones are on the ground? How many bones are scary?"

The last two samples are from children who both asked three questions about the items pictured, with each question narrowing the attributes, thereby following the model questions. Martha wrote about her pet bunnies, while Andrew used items from a junk box to sort.

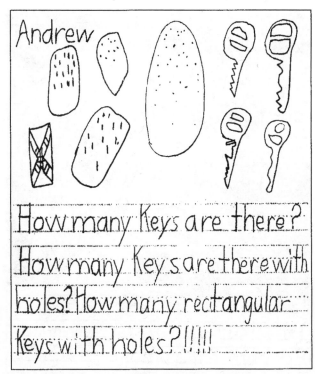

Martha drew and wrote about rabbits, and said, "How many rabbits were there? How many rabbits were flopty-eared? How many rabbits were flopty-eared and brown?"

How many rabbits were there? How many rabbits were flopet ereader How many rabbits were flopet ereade and brown?

Andrew used keys, and his questions, like Martha's closely followed the format of the book.

How many keys are there? How many keys are there with holes? How many rectangular keys with holes?!!!!!

Putting the **levels of understanding** on a horizontal line, the children's work might be placed as follows:

Levels of Understanding

T-Cole	Gia	Leah Cam	Andrew Martha
▼	▼	▼	▼
The child depicts some of the items and asks or attempts to ask a question about the total number.	The child depicts the items and asks one or more questions which do not follow the pattern in the book.	The child depicts the items and poses questions that begin to follow the pattern in the book.	The child depicts the items and poses three questions that completely follow the pattern in the book.

Extensions

This activity is a challenging one for the children. Depending on your class, you may opt to do more modeling of the questions in large group activities. If each child in your class brings in a hat, your could read the book *Hats, Hats, Hats* and then have the class ask questions about the hats they brought to class. To help children see attributes in common items, the books listed in the references help children develop the language necessary to sort and classify into increasingly smaller groups.

References

Giganti, Paul. *How Many Snails?* New York: Greenwillow Books, 1994.

Hoban, Tana. *Is It Rough? Is It Smooth? Is It Shiny?* New York: Greenwillow Books, 1984.

Kahalewai, Marilyn. *Whose Slippers Are Those?* Honolulu: The Bess Press, 2005.

Miller, Margaret. *Whose Shoes?* New York: HarperCollins Publishers, 1991.

Morris, Ann. *Hats, Hats, Hats.* New York: HarperCollins Publishers, 1993.

Reid, Margarette S. *The Button Box.* New York: Penguin Group USA, 1995.

How Many Wheels?

Materials

- Unifix cubes, wooden cubes, or other counting materials
- *10 for Dinner* by Jo Ellen Bogart (optional)
- Unlined paper
- Pencils, crayons, and/or colored marking pens
- Overhead projector
- Screen
- Overhead transparencies of children's work
- Post-it notes (optional)

Note

Although it is not necessary for children to hear *10 for Dinner* to solve the problem of How Many Wheels?, the book contains other possible opportunities for math problems. Other math lessons might have children graph favorite party foods, find possible combinations for 10, or figure out elapsed time from when the first until the last guest arrives.

Overview

Children use their knowledge of wheels on bicycles and cars to find out how many wheels are necessary to take children home from a party. The answers to this problem can vary depending upon the child's interpretation of the question. Allow 45 to 60 minutes for children to complete this problem.

Description

In the story, *10 for Dinner* by Jo Ellen Bogart, Margo asks ten children to come to her house for dinner on her birthday. The story ends with: "When the party was over, 5 guests went home in cars, 2 rode home on their bikes, and 2 went on foot. But 1 guest stayed to help with the dishes." After reading the book to the children, reread the page about how the children went home. However, **do not show them the picture in the book**. Then, ask the children to think about how many wheels may have taken the nine children home.

Review the facts and the question with the children as you write the following on the chalkboard:

> **5 children went home in cars.**
> **2 children rode home on bikes.**
> **2 children walked.**

How many wheels took the children home? Draw and/or write to explain your answer.

Make sure that all the children can explain the problem and know how many children walked, how many rode bikes, and how many rode in cars. Then, ask the children to think about how many wheels took the children home from the party. Explain that they may work with a partner to find the answer, but that each person must prepare his or her own report to the class. Counting materials (i.e., unifix cubes or color tiles) should be available to help the children solve this problem.

As the children work, observe and record the approaches they use to solve the problem. When they have finished their reports, make overhead transparencies of the various solutions. Be sure that this selection includes a variety of solutions to the problem (8 wheels, 12 wheels, 16 wheels, 20 wheels, or 24 wheels) as well as different ways to find those solutions (using cubes, counting, drawing the vehicles).

As the children share their experiences, be sure to emphasize that this one problem can have several solutions. Encourage the class to celebrate the diverse ways to look at and solve this problem.

For kindergarten children, simplify the problem so that it is developmentally appropriate for your class. You may wish to begin with a discussion of how many wheels there are on one car. The first time you try this problem, the question could be:

If five children came to school in 3 cars, how many wheels took them? How many children rode in each car?

Kindergarten children may want to use materials from the block corner to actually act out this problem. You can build the outline of three cars with blocks and place the children in them so that they can more easily see the total number of wheels and the different ways the children could ride in various cars.

Student Responses and Assessment:

As the children explore this problem, focus on these questions to note each child's learning preferences:

• Is the child able to understand and solve both parts of the problem (the number of wheels and the placement of the children)?

• Does the child use manipulatives to help solve the problem?

• Can the child explain to you orally his or her thoughts about the problem?

• Can the child express himself or herself clearly by either drawing or writing about the solution?

• Does the child have a unique way of looking at or solving the problem?

Some children will want to work alone, while others will prefer to work with a partner. Either is perfectly acceptable for primary grade children. It is interesting to note how individual children's preferences evolve throughout the year.

In the primary grade classroom, most children are able to solve this problem. The **levels of understanding** (from the least to the greatest grasp of understanding) you might find from a range of student responses may look like this:

Levels of Understanding

▼	▼	▼
The child depicts some wheels and/or children, but either does not address the mathematics OR does not solve any part of the problem correctly.	**The child depicts the correct number of children, but not the correct number of wheels; OR the child depicts the correct number of wheels, but not the correct number of children.**	**The child depicts both the correct number of wheels and children to arrive at one possible solution to the problem.**

Responses from kindergarten children to a modified problem also fit on this continuum. Their problem about wheels was:

If five children came to school in 3 cars, how many wheels took them? How many children rode in each car?

The kindergarten children answered their problem in small groups of six to eight children by drawing pictures. The children dictated their solutions to the teacher which she wrote on post-it notes.

The variety of correct responses often surprises primary grade children who are used to one correct answer. Typical responses from these grades and their **levels of understanding** are shown in the examples that follow. Cassie, Leah, and Ashley are at the most basic level of understanding.

Cassie's work is on the first level of understanding, as she did not solve even part of the problem correctly. She depicted three cars and some of the wheels. "Two kids came in three cars with six wheels," is what this kindergarten child dictated to the teacher.

Leah, a first grader, is also at this same level. Her work depicts cars and children, but neither were the correct number to solve the problem. Even after the teacher questioned her about the number of wheels, she insisted that there were only eight wheels total on the four cars. She ignored the bike riders and is missing one person riding in cars.

Ashley's response clearly fits the first level. She uses unifix cubes to depict the wheels, but does not solve even part of the problem correctly. When this second grader shared she added that the 37 stood for the number of wheels.

On the second level, the child depicts the correct number of children, but not the correct number of wheels; OR the child depicts the correct number of wheels, but not the correct number of children.

Katie, a second grader, depicted the correct number of wheels, but not the correct number of children. There are 12 wheels in her picture, but 10 children. She had trouble matching the number of children with their method of returning from the party.

Nick also depicted the correct number of wheels, and ignored completely any mention of the children involved. This first grader even included an equation for finding the number of wheels.

Kindergartners Kacey and Juan both placed the five children in the correct number of cars, but could not tell the correct number of wheels.

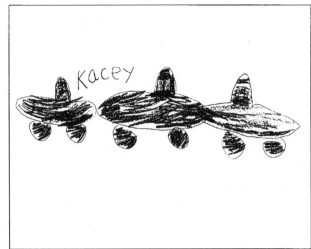

Kacey's placement of children in the cars and her confusion about the number of wheels was evident in the picture and in her dictation to the teacher: " Two kids went in one car, and two kids went in one car, and one kid went in one car, " she answered confidently, but when questioned about the number of wheels, she asked, "Is it 20? Then is it 14? How about 15?"

Juan's picture shows the five children in the three cars, but when his teacher asked about the number of wheels for the three cars he replied, "Four wheels." The teacher then tried to get him to revise his answer by saying, "There are four wheels on one car, how many on three cars?" Juan, however, remained firm with his original answer of four wheels.

In the following responses, all the children reach acceptable answers, and are able to justify the number of wheels and show how the children were placed. Their work is on the highest **level of understanding**.

Both Russell and Luis' work and J.J.'s work show the answer of 16.

Russell and Luis drew pictures of the three cars and two bicycles, showing the correct number of children. They wrote an equation oft 8 + 8 = 16 to stand for the number of wheels. "The first 8," explained Russell, "stands for the wheels on one car and two bikes, and the second 8 stands for the wheels on two cars."

J.J. numbered the wheels to make the total of wheels clear. When she brought her work to the teacher, she had not shown how many children rode in each car. The teacher asked her about this, and she returned to her desk to label each car with the number of "kids." She wrote, "When you count one pair of two wheels, you will see that there is 16."

Mayra wrote an equation about the answer that is confusing. When she shared her work with the class, she clarified her answer by saying that the five in the number sentence stood for the 5 cars rather than the 20 wheels.

Rocky's work is on the highest level of understanding when he depicts both the correct number of wheels and children to arrive at one possible solution to the problem. His picture shows two children in one car, two in another, and one in the third car. When relating the number of wheels to his teacher, Rocky counted the wheels and said, "Twelve wheels. Eight plus four is twelve."

If we take the student work for these kindergarten, first and second grade children and plot it on a horizontal continuum, it would look like this:

Levels of Understanding

Cassie Leah Ashley ▼	Kacey Juan Nick Katie ▼	J.J. Russell & Luis Mayra Rocky ▼
The child depicts some wheels and/or children, but either does not address the mathematics OR does not solve any part of the problem correctly.	The child depicts the correct number of children, but not the correct number of wheels; OR the child depicts the correct number of wheels, but not the correct number of children.	The child depicts both the correct number of wheels and children to arrive at one possible solution to the problem.

Extensions

An extension of the original problem for first and second grade children might be:

Six children arrived at Acacia (substitute your school name) School. They walked, rode their bikes, or rode in a car. Twenty wheels took them. How might they have come to school?

This extension is a more difficult version of the first problem because the children have to work backward and divide the number of wheels into an appropriate amount of vehicles. A group of first grade children also answered the extension question, with divergent responses. This is a harder problem, and many of the children struggled a bit before coming up with a response.

References

Bogart, Jo Ellen. *10 for Dinner*. New York: Scholastic, 1989.

What Fits Inside The Mitten?

Materials

- Small items from the classroom
- A mitten or sock for each pair of children
- Unifix cubes, wooden cubes, or other counting materials
- *The Mitten* by Jan Brett or by Alvin Tresselt
- Unlined paper
- Pencils, crayons, and/or colored marking pens
- Overhead projector (optional)
- Screen (optional)
- Overhead transparencies of children's work (optional)
- Post-it notes (optional)
- Chart paper labeled **Math Measurement Words** (optional)

Overview

Children choose five to ten items from the classroom that might fit inside a mitten. After they order the items by size from the smallest to the largest, they put the items into a mitten to see if they all can fit. The answers to this problem will vary, depending on the children's choice of items. It will likely take two or three forty-minute blocks of time to complete this lesson.

Description

In the story, *The Mitten* by Jan Brett, Niki loses a white mitten in the snow. A mole finds it and climbs inside. Larger and larger animals progressively climb inside until the mitten is stretched out of shape. When the bear sneezes, the animals and the mitten are scattered into the air.

After reading or telling the story to the children, discuss what happened to the mitten. Show the children a mitten or a sock. Ask what things in the classroom might fit into either the sock or mitten. List these items on the chalkboard. Then ask them which animals in the story first went into the mitten. Which went in the mitten last? Was there a difference in the sizes of the items? Then ask them about each item listed on the chalkboard. Which is the smallest? Which is the largest? Which items would fit in between?

Tell the children they are going to work with a partner to choose some items from the classroom to put in the mitten. When they have gathered the actual items, they arrange them in order from smallest to largest and record the order on the blank paper. Then, they will put each item in the mitten, beginning with the smallest and increasing in size until no more items will fit. When the mitten is full, ask children to create a written or pictorial list of the items that actually fit in the mitten.

Expect plenty of conversation as the children explore this task. It can be a difficult task to order objects by size when they each have a different shape. As the children work, note their level of measurement skills and use of comparison vocabulary. At the conclusion of the lesson, be sure to have the children report their findings to the class.

The next day, reread the book. Show the children a mitten or sock and ask if they can predict how many unifix cubes (or Teddy bear counters, wooden cubes, or any of the same small item) might fit in. Then explain the following task.

With a partner, students will predict how many of the objects that they choose will fit inside the mitten or sock. Then, they will record their estimates. Finally, they will find out the actual number by stuffing the mitten or sock with as many of their chosen objects as it can hold.

To record this experience, give each child a blank sheet of paper, even though they will work in pairs. It is fascinating to observe the various ways that kindergarten and first grade students will record this problem. Some outline the sock or mitten and draw the unifix cubes inside. Others attempt to write the words and put the numerals beside it. As the children finish, paper clip the sock or mitten to the recording sheet to save for the next day's lesson.

On the third day, have some of the children share their results. Then choose a group that used a small mitten and one that used a large mitten to compare the amount of cubes each held. As each group shares, ask the class if they can predict the amount of cubes that the other mitten will hold. Then have the children trade mittens (or socks) and redo the experiment, using knowledge from the previous activity to predict the results. Explain to students that they will replicate the second day's activity with the same materials; however, they can change the size of the mitten or sock. After this experience, have the children either dictate, draw or write about their results and what they learned.

As the children share their experiences, be sure to emphasize that this particular problem can have several solutions. Encourage the class to celebrate the diverse ways to look at and solve this problem.

For kindergarten classrooms, simplify the problem to meet the development needs of your children. For example, you may want to have them look for only five or six items to sequence. An extension of the original problem for first and second grade children might be to have them use the same sock or mitten, but vary the results by using different kinds of materials to fill it. With the change in material used, the children should be able to predict the amount by comparing the size of the new material with the previous one. (Unifix cubes are larger than lima beans, so it should take more lima beans to fill the mitten).

Student Responses and Assessment

As the children explore this problem, make note of their experiences and ideas. This is an especially good lesson to use for informal discussion about measurement vocabulary. As you observe the children, focus on the following questions:

- What does the child know about ordering random objects by size?

- What mathematical vocabulary does the child use to express these ideas?

- Can the child explain to you orally his or her thoughts about the problem?

- Can the child express himself or herself clearly by either drawing or writing about the solution?

- Does the child have a unique way of looking at or solving the problem?

There should be lots of conversation with this task since the objects the children choose will not have common attributes that are easily measured and compared. Teachers found it helpful to have a piece of chart paper labeled **Math Measurement Words** to list the words that the children used to describe the size differences in their items. This chart may then be expanded and used by the children as they continue to write during mathematics lessons.

In one kindergarten class, students worked with partners to find five items from the classroom to fit in their mitten. They were then asked to order the items from smallest to largest and record that order in some way. In this classroom, the children chose to trace the items, which sometimes made it difficult to distinguish its true identity. The teacher often asked, "What is this?" about the tracings as the children were working, and prodded the children to make their tracings look more like the actual items. When one pair of children were tracing around a toy pig from the farm animals collection, the teacher asked, "How will I know when I look at this later that this is a pig?" The children responded by drawing legs and other features on the pig. In other instances, the children dealt with this question by trying to label each item with invented spelling.

The teacher also posed the question, "Why do you think this _____ is smaller than _____?" Many kindergarten children were certain of the order, but had difficulty communicating why. The task of comparing the attributes of length, width, and height was sometimes confusing because the items they chose were not of a uniform shape. They often focused only on one attribute, such as length. In this class of thirty-two students, each pair was able to agree upon an order from smallest to largest and record it.

In one first and second grade classroom, the teacher chose to read the story and have the children choose ten items the first day of the lesson. The children saved the items in a baggie for the next day, when they ordered them by size. In any of the lessons in this book, use your judgment about the length of the lesson. If you have a class that needs extra time, extend the length of the lesson or continue with the lesson on the next day. It is important to listen to the children as they work and take the cue from them.

The conversation that children have in this lesson is especially important. It is a good time to emphasize the importance of vocabulary. Lindy and Leah, for example, struggled to decide which was smaller, a one-inch square tile or the square orange pattern block. When they approached their teacher with this dilemma, she asked them to look each item over carefully and then decide themselves. Five minutes later they came back to report that the tile was smaller because the pattern block seemed the same size but was actually thicker. During the discussion with the whole class, the girls shared this and the word "thicker" to the Math Measurement Word list.

Typical responses from kindergarten, first and second grade children as they sequenced the items in increasing size are shown in the examples that follow. While all children were able to complete this task successfully, they varied greatly in their ability to describe their solutions. Some children chose to trace the number of actual items, while others drew the items freehand and wrote about the order. The sophistication of their work can be shown in the **levels of understanding** (from the simplest to the most complex):

Levels of Understanding

▼	▼	▼	▼
The child traces or draws the items in order from smallest to largest.	The child traces or draws and then labels the items in order.	The child depicts the items in order and writes or tells about them.	The child depicts the items in order, and gives some mathematical insight(s) about the process.

Kindergartners Kirsten and Jennifer, on the first level of understanding, simply traced around each of their five items from smallest to largest: a calf, a cow, the letter "S", a crayon, and a bed.

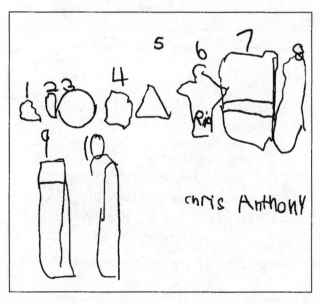

First graders Chris and Anthony traced around the items and numbered them beginning with the smallest. Their work shows the first level of understanding for this problem.

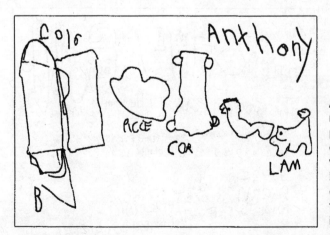

Anthony and Joel, both kindergartners, began at the right of their paper and traced a lamb, rooster, car, rock, and bed. They used invented spelling to label most of their items. This work depicts the second level of understanding because they traced and labeled the items in order.

The Mitten Sizes

Samuel
Nicholas

chalk   crayon   parallelogram

Samuel and Nicholas went one step further and began to number their items in addition to labeling them. This response also illustrates the second level of understanding.

The Mitten Sizes   Gia Kirsten

The Sallets is chalk The Soceaed Sallets is fome. The E is a Book The 4 Bigets is a unifix cube The 2 Bigets is my Eresea. The 6 Bigets is a crayon The 7 Bigets is a The Tile The 8 Bigtes is a Patuenn The 9 Bigets is a Crad. The 10 Bigets is a Srepiner.

Gia and Kirsten used only words and estimated spelling to describe their order, depicting the items in order and telling about them.

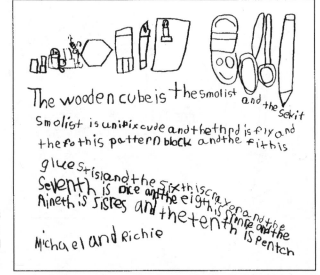

The wooden cube is the smolist and the sekit smolist is unifix cude and the thpd is fly and the fo this pattern block and the fit his glue stis land the sixth is cra yona nd the Seventh is Dice and the eigt his trinee and the Aineth is sisres and the tenth is Pentch

Michael and Richie

Michael and Richie drew the items and then wrote about their order. Their work also illustrates the third level of understanding.

Aimee Tokin
Kali fox
1 eraser
2 unifix coob
3 squar
4 Oilpastel
5 Sharpenr
6 gluestic
7 crayon
8 pensle
9 paint Brush
10 Sisers

I pickt out by loohing at then
veney cafly and putthem in ordel.

The next two examples depicted the items in order, and gave some mathematical insights about the process.

Aimee and Kali numbered and drew their responses and told how they made their choices.

The mitten Sizes   Megan
                                    Ashley
1 wooden cube ▢
2. pattern bloock △
3 chalk ⬭
4. E raser ▭
5. sharpiner ▯
6. unifix cubes ▭
7. crayon ▭
8. colored pencil ▭
9 Glue stick ▭
10. scissors ✂

It was hard to decide frist and last.
There was lots things allmost the Same.

The crayon and the colored pencil looked alike.
It was hard to decide if the wooden cube
or the pattern block went first.

Megan and Ashley talked about the difficulty of their choices.

If we plot the children's work on a horizontal continuum, it would look like this:

Levels of Understanding

Chris & Anthony Kristen & Jennifer ▼	Anthony & Joel Samuel & Nicholas ▼	Michael & Richie Gia & Kirsten ▼	Megan & Ashley Aimee & Kali ▼
The child traces or draws the items in order from smallest to largest.	The child traces or draws and then labels the items in order.	The child depicts the items in order and writes or tells about them.	The child depicts the items in order, and gives some mathematical insight(s) about the process.

Extensions

A group of first and second grade children also answered this extension question, which is related to the story *The Mitten*. You may want to try this question with your students.

> **Grandma knit mittens for Michael and 11 of his friends. How many fingers and toes would it take to fill those 12 pair of mittens? Use pictures, words, and/or diagrams to find your answer.**

The children answered this question in divergent ways. This is a difficult problem, and many of the children struggled a bit before coming up with a response.

References

Brett, Jan. *The Mitten*. New York: Putnam Juvenile; Boardbook edition, 2002.

Tresselt, Alvin. *The Mitten*. New York: HarperCollins Publishers, 1989.

Crazy Mixed-Up Animals

Materials

- Unifix cubes in various colors
- *Boo Whoo?* **or** *New at the Zoo 2* **or** *All Mixed Up* by Kees Moerbeek **or** *Mix & Match Educational Book Set*
- One copy per child of each of the mixed up animals duplicated on construction paper: pig—pink paper lamb—white paper cat—orange paper fox—brown paper
- Scissors
- Staplers
- Unlined paper
- Pencils, crayons, and/or colored marking pens
- Overhead projector (optional)
- Screen (optional)
- Overhead transparencies of selected children's work (optional)

Overview

In this problem, children are asked to see how many "crazy" animals they can make as they mix up the heads and bodies of a cat, a fox, a pig and a lamb. If three animals are used, there will be 9 possible combinations, and when a fourth animal is added, the possibilities increase to 16. Allow at least two extended math periods for this lesson.

Description

Begin by reading one of the Kees Moerbeek books to the children. In each of the books, there is a separation between the head and the bodies of the animals, making it possible to create other combinations of animals, such as an animal with a cat head and a pig body. After reading the book, use it to create some of these crazy mixed-up animals. Have the children describe the animals you make.

While the children watch, cut around the outside solid lines of the pig and the fox that were duplicated on construction paper. Then cut carefully on the middle solid line of each, but do not cut through the dotted line. Staple the two animals together near the dotted line so they will open up, as illustrated.

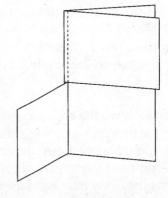

After the two animals are stapled, show the children the possible combinations that you can make from them: fox head, fox body; fox head, pig body; pig head, pig body; pig head, fox body. Ask them to count with you the number of different animals you can make. Then, have the children tell how they might draw or write to record the various possibilities as you carry out their instructions on the chalkboard. One child might tell you to write the names and body parts, while another child may have you draw the various combinations. Still another child may have you use first initials for the combinations.

Next, cut out and add the cat to your sample. Show some of the possible combinations, and have the children think of others. Tell them that there are nine possible real and mixed-up animals they can make. Their job is to find all nine and record them after they each make their own book using the cat, the fox and the pig. Have the materials ready and dismiss the children to begin the task. Remind them that after their own book is made, they need to find and keep a record of all nine of the possible combinations.

As the children work, encourage them to make sure each animal they record is a new one. Ask them if they have discovered a pattern that might make their job easier. Have unifix cubes available for the children to use if some of them would like to build the combinations. The following colors might be selected to represent the animals:

> **lamb—white cubes**
> **cat—orange cubes**
> **pig—red cubes**
> **fox—brown cubes**

It may take the children forty-five minutes to an hour to complete this task. Have a place for them to put their finished records and tell them to save their mixed-up animal books for the next day's lesson. When all the children have finished their work, choose a few representative samples for the children to share on the overhead the following day.

The next day, have the children explain their solutions for this problem using the overhead projector and transparencies. Be sure to have the children point out any organizational strategies or patterns that they may have used.

Then show the children how to add the lamb to their book. If the lamb is added as the last page, it is not necessary to cut between the head and the body. Now tell the class that their job is to find all the possible animal combination and tell how they know that they have found all of them. (With the three animals the day before, the total number was given to them.) Hand each child the

lamb and a blank piece of paper as you dismiss them to begin working.

Again, observe the children as they work. Take note of how the children approach the task, and look for children who use patterns as part of their solution strategies. Make overhead transparencies of selected samples of student work.

As the children share their work, question them to fully explain their thinking. If there is time and the class is still focused, encourage other children to share their solutions and ideas.

With kindergarten children, introduce this activity in small groups. Begin with two animals, and then show the children how to make their own books with three animals. After the children have each made their own book, have the group work together to find all nine of the animals. Have the children find ways to prove that they have all nine animals. For most kindergarten classes, finding the nine ways will be enough of a challenge. A few children may be ready to add the fourth animal.

Student Responses and Assessment

This is a difficult problem that needs to be modeled carefully by the teacher. With three animals, it is helpful to tell the children that there are nine possible combinations. One teacher had her children discuss the nine animals and determine the number that were real and the number that were pretend. Her class defined "real" as those animals that we might find in our world, such a pig head with a pig body.

When first and second grade children add the fourth animal, challenge them to predict the number of possible combinations. You may want to tell your students that there are more than twelve ways. (The actual exact number is sixteen). Children will work for a long time on this task. They need an uninterrupted block of time to do a thorough job of checking for duplicate animals. In a class of 32 first and second grade children, it is likely that over half of the children will find all 16 combinations! It is not an unrealistic expectation for the rest of the children to get 12 or more! Emphasize the organization style and success of the first day's experience before adding the fourth animal.

Kindergarten children solve this problem best in small groups. One kindergarten teacher found it more concrete for her children to actually cut the heads apart from the bodies. Each child then put their heads and bodies in a group pile and the children created the various animals together from the pile. There were unifix cubes available in the colors of the animals for the children to use also. She found that working together, the groups were all able to make seven to nine of the combinations with three animals.

In another kindergarten class, the children worked with a skeleton, ghost, and witch to find mixed-up monsters. In both of these classes, the children's work would fit on the following continuum, or **levels of understanding,** as would the work of first and second grade students. This continuum is appropriate for total combinations of either nine or sixteen mixed-up animals.

Levels of Understanding

The child depicts less than half of the combinations possible.	The child depicts half or more of the combinations. Some of the combinations may be duplicated.	The child represents all the combinations of the task without duplications in a guess and check or random fashion.	The child shows an organized and systematic representation of all the possible combinations.

Patrick, a first grader, depicts less than half of the combinations. His drawing shows four of the nine animals completed successfully. He is on the most basic level of understanding.

Ryan, another first grader on the second level of understanding, depicts more than half of the sixteen combinations on his paper and stated, "You can make 10 animals."

Kristen, a kindergarten child, chose to draw her solution and found seven possible combinations out of nine. Like Ryan, she is on the second level.

In the next six samples, all the children have the correct number of combinations – either nine or sixteen. They are all at the third and fourth level of understanding.

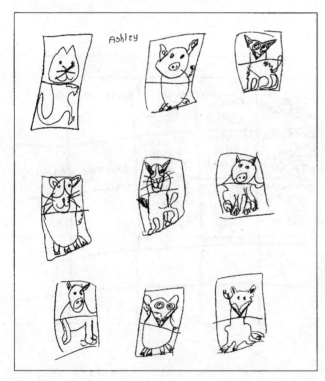

Ashley P., a first grader, drew all nine ways on one side of the paper. On the other side she wrote, using estimated spelling, "I found out there are 9 ways to make the animals by counting my fingers." Because Ashley's work is organized in a random fashion, she is at the third level of understanding.

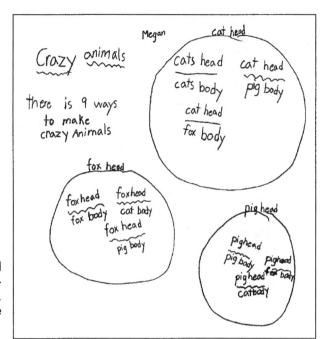

Megan, a second grader, created an organized list, grouping the animals by the kind of head they had. Her organization puts her at the fourth level of understanding.

Aja's and Richard's organization is not as evident as Megan's but if you look closely you can see a pattern to their drawings. As the children shared their samples, some borrowed ideas from the sharing and applied it to their next task.

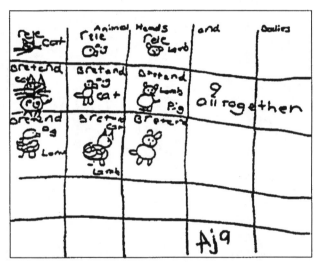

Aja, a first grader, labeled her animals and organized them by whether they were real or pretend animals.

Richard gave each animal a name based on their body parts. His drawing shows three cat heads, then three pig heads and finally three lamb heads.

Again the organization is evident as Ashley S. and Richard worked with the harder task of sixteen combinations.

As these examples show, discussing the children's work is a vital part of the learning process. Often the very next day, you can see the results of the previous lesson as the children adapt or use the ideas that their classmates have shared.

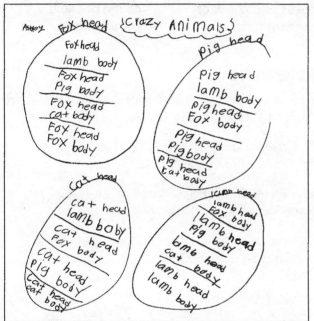

Ashley S., a second grader, used Megan's idea of grouping the animals by their heads when she worked with four animals.

Richard, however, painstakingly drew every single animal. His organization follows his previous style for the three mixed-up animals.

If we put the children's work on a horizontal continuum, it might look like this:

Levels of Understanding

Patrick	Kristen Ryan	Ashley P.	Ashley S. Richard Aja Megan
▼	▼	▼	▼
The child depicts less than half of the combinations possible.	The child depicts half or more of the combinations. Some of the combinations may be duplicated.	The child represents all the combinations of the task without duplications in a guess and check or random fashion.	The child shows an organized and systematic representation of all the possible combinations.

The main goal of this activity is that children learn to see things in new and different ways. It is less important that the children arrive at the exact answer. You will also be able to observe a child's ability to check back and see if a combination has already been recorded. Mathematical persistence is another factor that will help students to solve this problem. Organization in their recording is also important. Be sure to give children enough time to complete and check their work; many children take more than one class period to find and record all sixteen examples.

Extensions

The book *Boo Whoo?* contains spooky Halloween characters such as a ghost, a mummy, and a skeleton. In addition to trying the mixed up animals, use the Halloween blacklines of the witch, skeleton, scarecrow, and ghost to provide another experience for your children in finding combinations.

You may also want to make your own combinations to fit units of study. You can also mix and match the characters of a favorite fairy tale: Little Red Riding Hood, the wolf, Grandma, and the woodcutter. To do this, start with the same basic outline and make sure the neck area on each character matches, as illustrated here.

References

Author Unknown. *Mix & Match Educational Book Set.* Atlanta, GA: Dalmatian Press.

Moerbeek, Kees. *All Mixed Up.* Los Angeles: Price Stern Sloan, 1994.

Moerbeek, Kees. *Boo Whoo?* Los Angeles: Price Stern Sloan, 1993.

Moerbeek, Kees. *New at the Zoo 2.* New York: Random House, 1993.

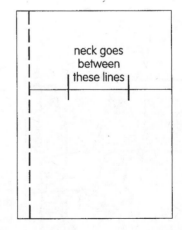

neck goes between these lines

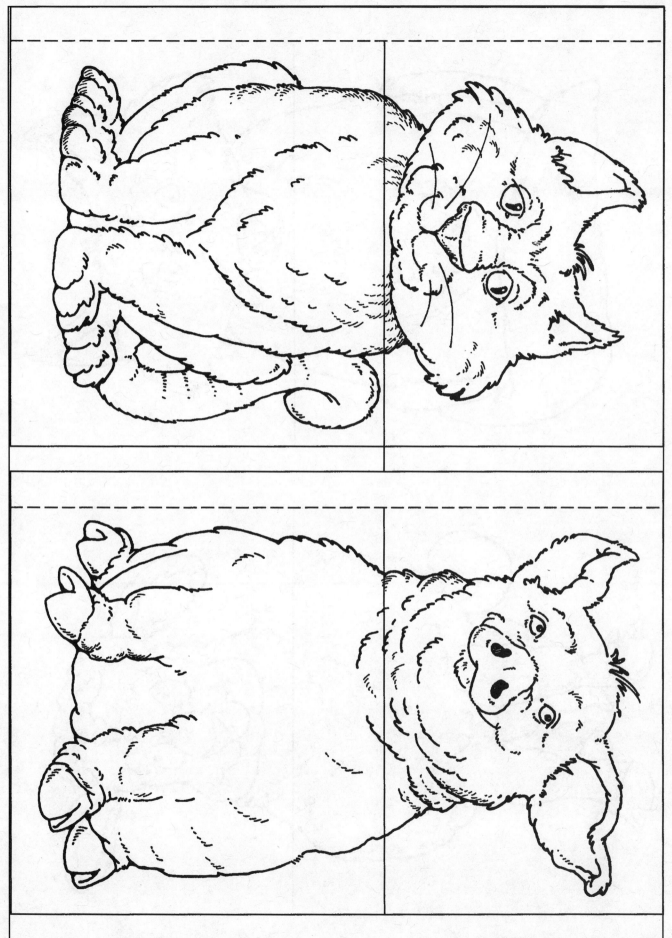

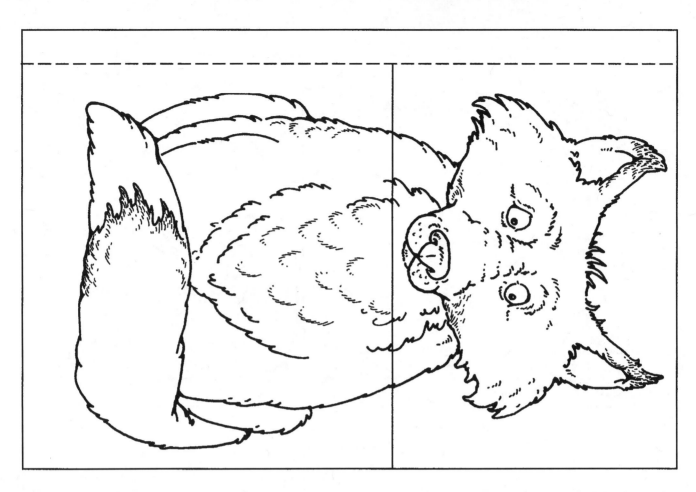

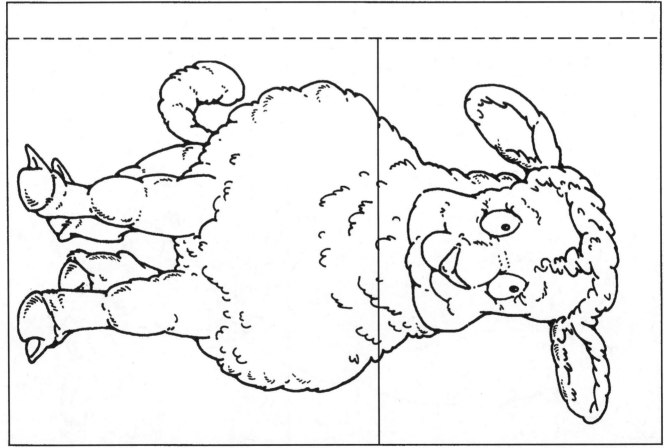

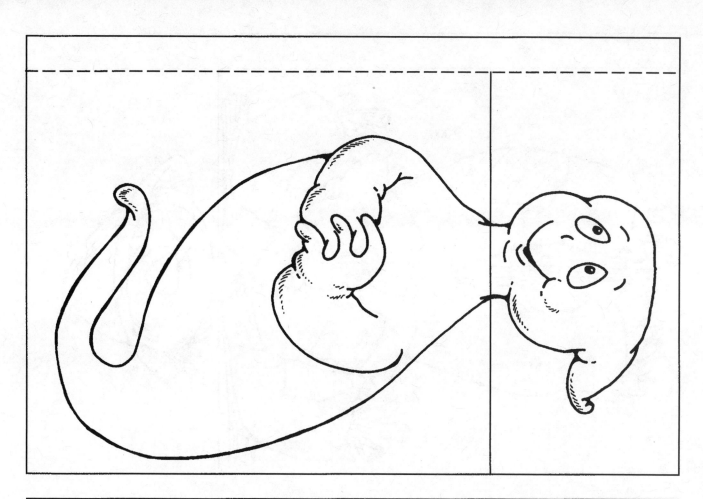

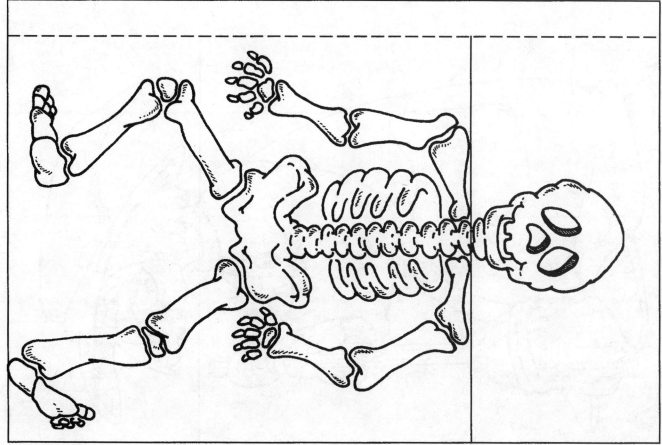

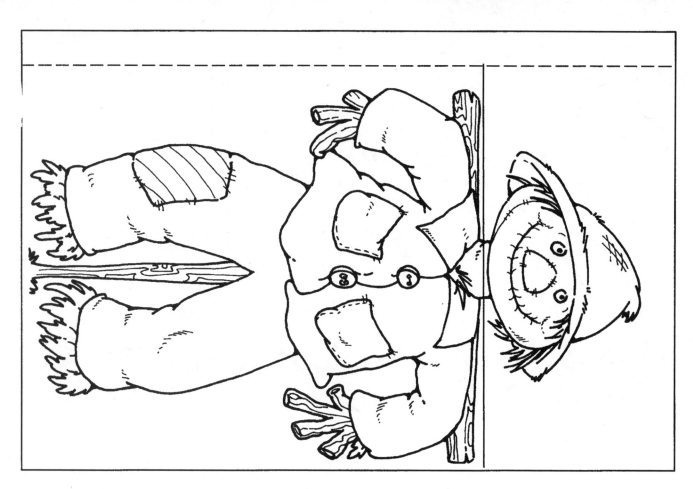

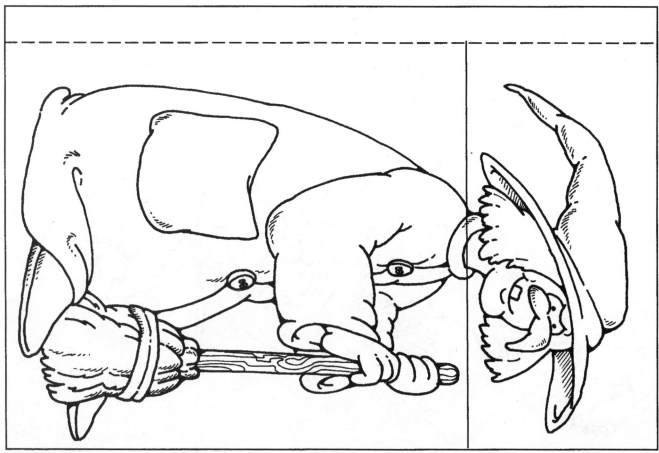

Safari Toss/Color Toss

Materials

- Unifix cubes or other counting materials
- One die per child
  Kindergarten —
  three-colored die
  1st and 2nd —
  animal die
- Unlined paper
- Pencils, crayons, and/or colored marking pens
- Overhead projector (optional)
- Screen (optional)
- Overhead transparencies of children's work (optional)
- Chart paper (optional for kindergarten)

Overview

This activity will span two or three days. During the first part of the lesson, the children collect data from rolling their die. In the second part, they interpret the data they collected. At **least** two 45 minute periods should be allowed to complete this investigation

Description

On the first day, model how to make the die. Tell children to first cut around the solid outside line and then cut carefully on the inside dotted lines. Show the children how to fold the die on the remaining solid lines toward the center with the animal pictures on the outside. Then tape the die when all six sides have an animal picture on them. This die can be easily made by first and second grade children if you carefully model the cutting and the folding. It is important that the children cut carefully and make sure the dotted lines are cut to the intersection exactly.

With kindergarten, have children color the die with three red sides, two green sides and one blue side. Depending on the time of the year, you may want to assemble the dice after they color them. The children can use the appropriate crayon to record their rolls, and can choose their own ways to organize this information. Children can also record the data with red, green and blue unifix cubes. Although first and second grade children can write about the resulting data, kindergarten children can discuss their results and their ideas can be recorded on chart paper. Or, adults or older students interview the children individually about their data and take dictation about their ideas.

After first and second graders have made the dice, provide time for the class to experiment with them. In about twenty minutes, call the children back together to discuss the results of their experiments. Children can share what they did with the die and what they found out. They may or may not have decided to record the results of this exploration.

On the second day, emphasize data collection. Ask the children to roll their dice 50 or more times and devise a system to record the results of each roll. Each child should have a blank piece of paper and pencil or crayon to record their rolls. It is important that children generate the ideas for recording the data. Therefore, do not model your method of keeping track of the rolls. If you do model one method, it is likely that each child's record will look just like yours. Allow the children ample time to roll and record their dice fifty or more times. Save the children's work for the next part of the lesson which can continue during an extended math period or on the following day.

Before the next lesson, look over the children's work. Find samples of a variety of record keeping methods. For instance, one child may have used tally marks, another may have used numbers, and still another may have drawn pictures of the animals. Select five or six samples and ask the children whose work you have chosen if they are willing to share with the whole class. If possible, make overhead transparencies of the samples.

Begin this part of the lesson by having the children share their methods for keeping track of their rolls. Be sure to emphasize that there is not necessarily one best way to collect this data.

After the five or six children have shared, allow other children to add ideas if time permits. Then, ask the children what they noticed about the results of the data. Did one animal come up more often on the die? After a brief discussion, explain that each child will use his or her data from the previous lesson. They will look at this information and then write about what they learned. Give each child the results from the previous experiment and a blank sheet of paper, and ask them to begin.

As the children work, circulate throughout the room. If a child initially has difficulty with the task, you may want to ask, "Which animal got the least rolls? Why do you think that happened?" When all the children are finished, collect both papers.

For a final discussion, you may want to ask for volunteers to share their data records and their writing. Be sure to emphasize the positive aspects of each child's work. Older children can be challenged to think about the various recording methods and determine which were easiest to interpret and why.

This activity should be repeated throughout the year. To revisit the activity, change the pictures on the face of the die. On page 66 you will find a die for the holidays which has a bell on three faces, a candle on two faces, and a dreidel on one face. There is also a die for spring which has shamrocks and pots of gold on page 67. Each time you present the activity, look for more sophistication in the ways the children record data and report their results.

Student Responses and Assessment

There are two areas to address in assessing student work: data collection and data interpretation. The **levels of understanding** for the data collection part of this task are:

Data Collection Levels of Understanding

▼	▼	▼	▼
The child records the rolls of the die in a haphazard fashion so that it is impossible to decipher the data at a later time.	The child records the rolls of the die randomly, so that it is difficult to find the total number of rolls for each animal, but possible.	The child has a more organized method of recording the rolls. It is easy to see which animal has the most or least rolls, but it is more difficult to determine the total.	The child organizes the rolls of the die in an efficient manner, and it is easy to see the results and find a total.

Chad, a first grader, randomly recorded his rolls, without a plan. When he was asked to interpret the data the next day, he told the teacher he didn't know what he had written. He was at the first level of understanding because it was impossible to decipher his data.

Using the die with different colored faces, Christen made a mark on her paper using the matching color crayon for each roll of the die. She randomly placed the marks on her paper, making the task of finding the total number for each color difficult, but possible. She is at the second level of understanding.

Kali, a first grader, painstakingly drew each of the animals as she rolled the die. Because she put them in chronological order, it is difficult to tell at a glance which of the animals she rolled the most or least. She is also at the second level of understanding.

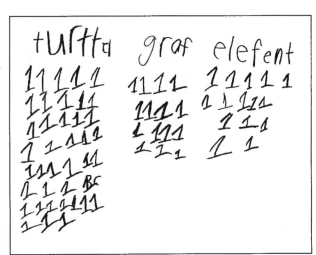

Nissa, another first grade student at the second level of understanding, had titles for each of the animals. She chose to mark a number one under an animal each time it was rolled. This also made it confusing to tell at a glance which animal had the most rolls, especially between the giraffe and the elephant.

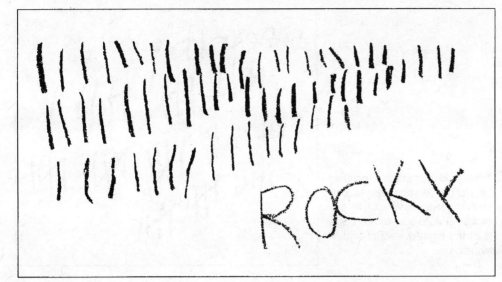

Rocky, a kindergarten child, used slash marks in appropriate colors to keep a record of his rolls of the die. He arranged his marks in rows according to the color, which makes it easy to see at a glance that red had the most rolls. It is not easy to tell, however, the exact amount of each color that was rolled. He is at the third level of understanding.

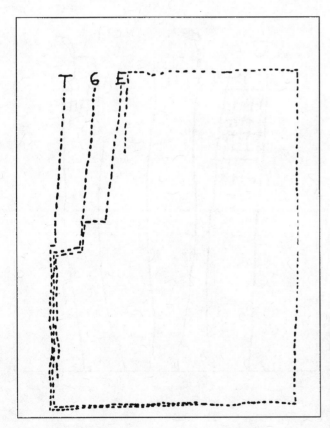

Craig, a second grade student, is also at the third level. Craig has a starting point for each animal under the first initial of the animal's name. He made a mark for each roll of the die under the appropriate animal letter. Note that the turtle marks go all around the outside of the paper.

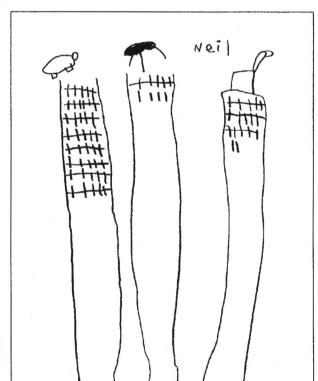

Tiffany, a kindergartner, organized her work in rows according to color and used tally counts each time to make her data easy to read. She is at the highest level of understanding.

Neil, a first grader, used tally counts of six to tell his rolls. Like Tiffany's, his work is on the highest level of understanding.

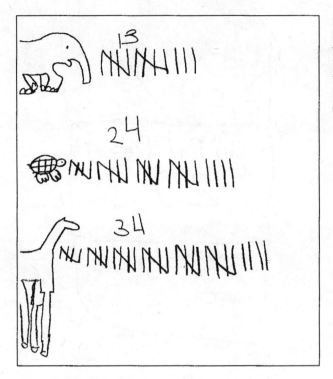

Laura organizes her work in a horizontal fashion and also uses tally marks. This second grader includes the total number of times each animal was rolled. Her work also illustrates the highest level of understanding.

The interpretation of the data also shows variety. The written or oral interpretation of some of the children is discussed below. The children's work for data interpretation has the following three levels:

Data Interpretation Levels of Understanding

▼   ▼   ▼ ⟶

The report contains little or no information about the data.

The report tells the number of times each one was rolled and/or which has the most, least and middle amounts.

The report tells about the number of times and/or which animal has most or least, and also relates this information to the number of times each animal is on the face of the die.

At the most **basic level of understanding,** Chad was not able to interpret the data from his report. In fact, he asked the teacher if he could redo his data collection. (This is explained at the end of this lesson.) After further questioning about her data, Christen was only able to say, "Look at all the reds I got." Because of her limited report, Christen is also at the **beginning level of understanding.**

Neil, a first grader, used tally counts of six to collect the data and then made a short report. The numbers in his report closely match his tally marks. His report shows the second level of understanding.

Nissa, another first grade child, used words to explain why the turtle had the most, the giraffes had "medium" and the elephant had "a little bit." She is at the highest level of understanding.

Tiffany reported the number of each color to her teacher. When questioned, this kindergartner was able to respond that, "red has most because there's three reds (sides)." She is at the **highest level of understanding**. Most second graders make a connection between the number of times the animal is featured on the die to the winning numbers, as evidenced by this report by Laura. In fact, she struggles with the idea that the turtle should have won, but didn't. Tiffany and Laura are both at the **highest level of understanding** because they express the idea that the number of times an animal is on the face of a die should relate to the amount of times it is rolled.

Laura

The elephant got 13. And the turtles got 24. The giraffes got 34. I think the giraffes got the most becuse maybe I was not rolling very good.

Lauria's work

If we plot the children on the levels of understanding for data interpretation, it would look like this:

Data Interpretation Levels of Understanding

Chad Christen	Neil	Tiffany, Nissa, Laura
▼	▼	▼
The report contains little or no information about the data.	The report tells the number of times each one was rolled and/or which has the most, least and middle amounts.	The report tells about the number of times and/or which animal has most or least, and also relates this information to the number of times each animal is on the face of the die.

As you compare each child's level of understanding for data collection with his/her ability to understand the data, you will see some variation with the two tasks. Nissa, for example, is on the highest level of understanding for the data interpretation, while her data collection method is still at the second level.

Data Collection Levels of Understanding

Chad	Christen Kali Nissa	Rocky Craig	Tiffany Neil Laura
▼	▼	▼	▼
The child records the rolls of the die in a haphazard fashion so that it is impossible to decipher the data at a later time.	The child records the rolls of the die randomly, so that it is difficult to find the total number of rolls for each animal, but possible.	The child has a more organized method of recording the rolls. It is easy to see which animal has the most or least rolls, but it is more difficult to determine the total.	The child organizes the rolls of the die in an efficient manner, and it is easy to see the results and find a total.

The discourse and learning that occurs as the children listen to one another during class discussions is crucial to this task and all open-ended activities. Children should be allowed to revise and/or begin again, based on what they learn from each other. They should also be allowed the time and space to struggle with the problem. Don't be alarmed if a child cannot make sense of his or her data on the second (or third) day of this lesson. Children often need many experiences before they become comfortable with this type of problem.

Chad, a young first grader in a combination first and second grade classroom, is a perfect example of what can happen if children are allowed the opportunity to make their own sense of things. On the first day, Chad made his die successfully and also began to record his data. As the teacher circulated around the room, she noticed that Chad's recording system did not seem to make a lot of sense. She paused and quietly asked him what the numbers on the paper meant. He looked at her, shrugged his shoulders, and kept on writing. At the end of 45 minutes of work, his paper (which you may remember as the first example) looked like this:

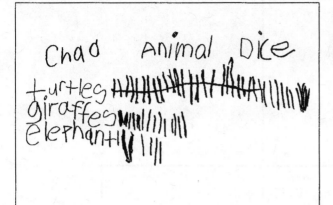

The teacher did not choose to highlight Chad's paper for discussion the next day. But, after the children had received their record of rolls and a paper for their report, Chad privately approached the teacher. He said that he didn't understand his record of the rolls he did the previous day and wanted to start over. The teacher gave him an new sheet of paper and he rolled his die again for more than 50 times. In that same period, Chad also had time to complete his data interpretation report. His new counting sheet and report is shown to the left.

Chad Animal Dice
turtles got most
giraffet mtol
elephant last

Given the chance, Chad was able to redo his work and make sense of the task. Chad had more opportunities that year to work with recording dice, and each time his ability to record and report his data increased in efficiency and sophistication. Children need opportunities to struggle with and make sense of mathematics in a risk-free environment. Revisiting this activity throughout the year gives children just such a chance.

Animal
Dice Pattern

Color
Dice Pattern

Red

Green

Green   Red   Blue

Red

Holiday
Dice Pattern

Dice Pattern

Birthday Candles

Materials

- Unifix cubes or other counting materials
- One package of 12 or 24 birthday candles (un-opened in a shrink wrapper, if possible)
- Unlined paper
- Pencils, crayons, and/or colored marking pens
- Overhead projector (optional)
- Screen (optional)
- Overhead transparencies of children's work (optional)

Overview

For this problem, children use addition and subtraction to find out if there are enough candles in the package for the birthdays that are pending. Allow at least 40 minutes for the children to draw and/or write their stories.

Description

In first and second grade, show the children the box of birthday candles. Have them examine the box to tell you the number of candles it holds. Then, tell them they are going to find out if there are enough candles in this box for three birthdays. After the problem is discussed, write the following on the chalkboard:

Your mother bought a box of 24 birthday candles. Next year your older sister will be 12 years old. You will be 7 years old. Your younger brother will be 4 years old. Will there be enough candles for all of your birthdays?

As you write, tell the children about the problem. Brainstorm ways they might find the answer.

For kindergartners, you can write the following problem on the board to build reading vocabulary. However, you'll need to include drawings and plenty of discussion to be sure that every child understands the problem:

There are 12 candles in the box. I have to make 2 birthday cakes. I need 5 candles for 1 cake and 6 candles for the other. If one box holds 12 candles, how many boxes do I need?

Before the children begin their work, remind them that they are to draw a picture, write a story, and/or show a number sentence about the birthday candles. With kindergarten children, have them draw their picture and dictate the story to you or another adult. Depending on the time of year, some first grade students may need to dictate their story to an older student or an adult.

As children finish writing or dictating their problems, you may want to make overheads of some of them. Then, have those children share their solution with the class. If you are working with kindergarten children, you may want to have the children share their results in the small groups when everyone has finished.

Student Responses and Assessment:

This problem was presented to kindergarten children at the beginning of the school year with interesting results. The teacher worked with small groups; the problem provided a revealing assessment of each child's ability to count and combine numbers. Many children could figure out the first part of the problem and knew that there were 11 candles on both cakes. However, many needed assistance to determine how many boxes of candles they needed. One child responded, "Why can't you just buy 2 boxes? Then you'll have enough." Candis counted the candles she drew on the paper and found there were 11. She responded, "I'll just ask my Mom and Dad. They'll know," when the teacher questioned her to find out if one box of candles was enough, perhaps revealing that she looks to adults for the answers.

In this same classroom, the children had previously worked with birthday candle explorations (from the book *Workjobs* by Mary Baratta Lorton), and some decided to use the real candles and birthday cake workmats from the workjobs box. Andy and Kristen worked collaboratively to solve the problem. They first counted out 12 candles. Andy took out a cake workmat and put 5 candles on it. He then put out another cake workmat and asked Kristen, "What would you put on this cake?" Kristen replied, "Six candles." After Kristen put out the six candles on a second cake, Andy identified the candle that was left by saying, "That's the twelfth one." On paper, Kristen then attempted to write a number sentence explaining what happened, by writing 11 - 1.

Although the difficulty of the problem varied by grade level, the levels of understanding for this problem were similar:

Levels of Understanding

The child depicts the content of the problem, but makes no reference to its mathematical elements.	The child depicts some of the mathematical elements of the problem.	The child shows that there are enough candles for all the birthdays.	The child shows there are enough birthday candles and states that there was one left in the package, or that only one package was necessary.

Children at the first level of understanding know that the problem is about birthday cakes and candles, but make no reference to its mathematical elements.

Breanna, a first grader, starts to copy the problem and then lists the colors that the candles might be. She does not try to solve the problem, but does draw a picture of the cake.

Noemi draws a child next to a cake with six candles on it.

At the second level, the children depicts or attempts to depict some of the mathematics of the problem.

Violetta attempts to create an equation with the future ages of each child, and confuses the word "doler" (dollars) for candles.

Randyl, a kindergartner, draws the two cakes and places the correct number of candles on each cake. In her dictation she states, "It's a pretty birthday cake and there is 5 and 6 birthday candles on it." Her picture accurately portrays the problem, but she does not mention of the total number of candles used or how many boxes of candles are needed.

At the third level, the child knows there are enough candles for all the birthdays.

Christel

The Candle Problem

I counted in my head and the answer I got was 23.

Christel draws all 23 candles on one cake, stated the total numbers, but does not compare this to the amount in the box.

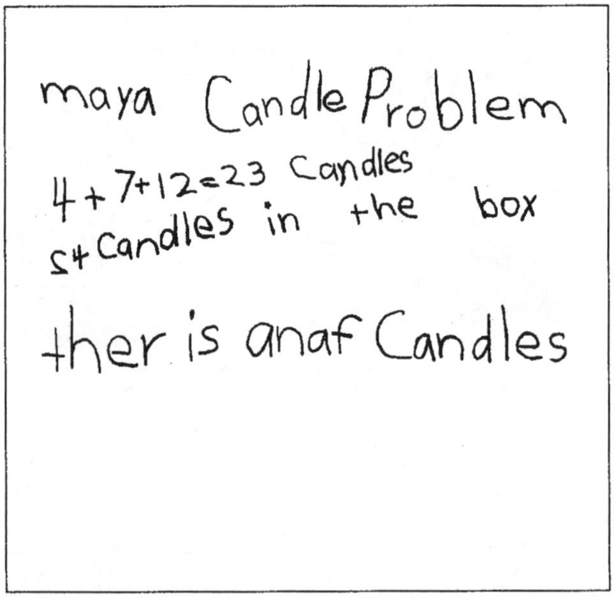

maya Candle Problem

4 + 7 + 12 = 23 Candles
54 Candles in the box

ther is anaf Candles

Mayra uses an equation to get the 23 and then states there is "anaf" (enough) candles.

At the fourth level, the child shows there are enough candles and states there is one left in the package, or that it only one package is necessary.

Kristen counts 12 actual candles on her mat and then draws them. She attempts to write a number sentence (11-1) to show her solution.

Joel candle Problem

yes the mom will have a nuf becuse 4 7 and 12 make 23 and ther is 1 axdu.

Joel, a second grader draws separate cakes with candles and knew there would be one "axdu." (extra)

If the children were placed at their levels of understanding of this problem, the developmental continuum would look like this:

Levels of Understanding

Brenna Noemi ▼	Violetta Randyl ▼	Christel Mayra ▼	Kristen Joel ▼
The child depicts the content of the problem, but makes no reference to its mathematical elements.	The child depicts some of the mathematical elements of the problem.	The child shows that there are enough candles for all the birthdays.	The child shows there are enough birthday candles and states that there was one left in the package, or that only one package was necessary.

This question provides the teacher with an opportunity to assess children's comfort with story problems. At the beginning of the school year, kindergarten children typically were so engrossed in finding the number of candles used that they had difficulty remembering to compare this number with the number of candles in the box. Teachers found that their children were willing to work on the problem, but usually were unable to consider both concepts concurrently. It was difficult for some children to combine the five and six to make eleven, while others were unable to count to six. The teacher was able to find out a lot about the children while they worked with this problem.

For first and second grade children, this problem was less difficult to solve, but the ease with which they solved it varied from child to child. Some children solved the problem in less than 15 minutes, while others pondered over the solution and took 40 minutes to find the answer. Another facet that the teacher found interesting was the ease in which some children wrote equations that fit the solution.

Extensions

Multiple step problems are not usually found in primary math textbooks. However, many children are able to solve these complex problems if they are presented within a meaningful, real life context. The format of birthday candle problem can be adapted to other problems for first and second grade children later in the year. For instance:

There are 27 children in our class. Chocolate chip cookies come in packages of 50. Will there be enough cookies in one package for all the children to have 2 cookies? Will there be some left over or will you need more cookies? How do you know? Draw and/or write about your answer.

References

Baratta-Lorton, Mary. *Workjobs II.* Menlo Park, CA: Addison-Wesley, 1979.

Sylvester's Pebbles

Materials

- Small rocks or pebbles of various sizes, shapes, colors and textures
- *Sylvester and the Magic Pebble* by William Steig or *Everybody Needs a Rock* by Byrd Baylor
- 5" by 8" file cards of pieces of paper
- Yarn loops (each 1 yard long)
- Chart paper
- Marking pen
- Unlined paper
- Pencils, crayons, and/or colored marking pens
- Overhead projector (optional)
- Screen (optional)
- Overhead transparencies of children's work (optional)
- Post-it notes (optional)

Overview

The children are asked to sort rocks in three or more ways. Three to four class sessions are needed to establish vocabulary and procedures for sorting and classifying the rocks. Allow forty to sixty minutes for each session.

Description

Either *Sylvester and the Magic Pebble* or *Everybody Needs A Rock* are books that can be used to introduce this problem. Read and discuss one of these books with the children. Have a chart ready that has the heading **Rocks can be...** Show the chart to the children and ask them to think of ways to describe rocks or pebbles to complete the chart. One class of first and second grade children came up with the adjectives pictured in the illustration.

Rocks can be...

lumpy   round   little

black   mossy   bumpy

triangular   flat   red

speckled   wet   white

big   holey   striped

smooth   dry   rough

blue   shiny   brown

Then, inform the children that part of their homework assignment is to bring in one or two rocks for the class to use on the next day. Limit the size of the rocks by telling the children that the rock must be small enough to fit inside the space made by connecting their thumb and forefinger.

For the lesson the next day, have blank 5" by 8" file cards, marking pens, yarn loops, and extra rocks ready for any children who need them. Tell the children to bring their rocks as they gather in your classroom meeting area. Review the chart from the previous day, and ask if there are more words they might need to describe their rocks. Add these new words to the chart. Then have the children read the words on the chart with you as you point to them. Ask the children to think of one word that describes their rock. Choose one child to share his or her choice. Write that word on a file card. Then choose another child and write that choice on a separate file card. Continue until you have from 16 to 20 cards. Have the class read the cards with you. As you are reading the words, ask the children to hold up their rock if it has the characteristic that you are reading.

Put two yarn loops on the floor next to each other, but do not overlap them. Ask the children sit in a large circle around the loops. Choose a description card randomly and place it on one of the yarn circles. Ask the children to read the word. If their rock(s) fit the description, have them put the rock in the circle. Then, choose another card. Place this on the other yarn loop. Have children put their rock in this loop if it matches the description. The floor area should look something like this :

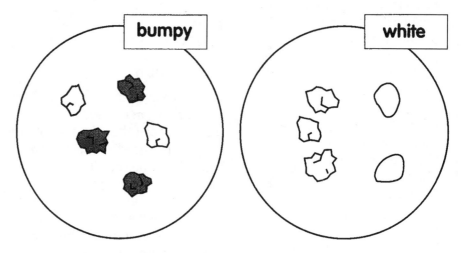

As students add rocks to the second loop, a child will likely say, "My rock is the bumpy pile, but it's white too." This is your opening to question the children about where that rock belongs because it is **both** bumpy and white. If a child does not provide the opportunity to initiate this discussion, then you may need to ask the children where they should put "the bumpy rock that is also white."

As you question children about where to place with the rock that belongs in both places (in this case the bumpy white, rock), ask the children for their solutions. They might suggest to: put that rock in the middle of the two circles or make a new yarn loop and label it as " bumpy and white." Both of these solutions are plausible and can be demonstrated. Then ask the children to think of a way to use the two the yarn loops and the two cards to show that the rock fits in both categories. Provide time for the children to suggest the idea of overlapping the yarn loops. If this does not happen, overlap the yarn loops yourself and ask the children what would belong in the over-lapped section. The yarn loops may look something like this:

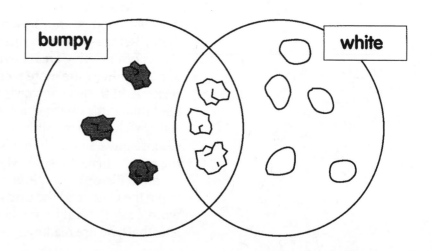

Discuss the characteristics the rocks need that belong in each section of the loops. Also, have children suggest where a rock would be placed if it were neither bumpy nor white (outside both loops).

When the children have had an opportunity to understand this diagram, remove the cards and rocks. Then, choose one new card to place on each of the yarn loops. For instance, one loop might now be labeled "smooth" and the other "speckled." This time, ask students where their rock belongs and how they know they are correct. Possible responses include, " My rock goes in this area because it is smooth and not speckled" or " My rock goes in both loops because it has speckles and is smooth."

On the third day of this lesson, continue working with the class to sort their rocks. Make sure the children place their rock correctly and tell how they know where to place it. Choose the cards randomly, and be sure to include children whose rocks might fit outside the loops. If it is easy for children to sort rocks in two loops, you may wish to add a third loop as a further challenge, as illustrated here.

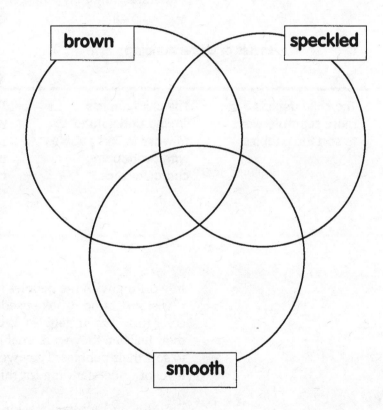

Additional ideas for sorting and classify may be found in the "Organizing Information" chapter in the *Mathematics Their Way Summary Newsletter* by Cynthia Garland.

After the children understand how to sort using two (or three) yarn loops, they are ready to complete the problem, which is:

> **Sylvester had 15 pebbles in his collection. Use pictures, diagrams, and words to describe 3 or more ways he might sort his pebbles.**

With kindergarten children, you may want to pose this problem in small groups. First and second grade children might all work on this at the same time. Actual rock or pebbles should be available for all children to use.

After the children have completed the assignment, discuss the possible solutions. If the children have written their answers, you may want to make overhead transparencies of them.

Student Responses and Assessment

As kindergarten, first, and second grade students work on this problem, the following levels of understanding may emerge:

Levels of Understanding

▼	▼	▼	▼
The child depicts less than 3 separate ways to sort the pebbles.	**The child depicts 3 or more separate ways to sort the pebbles.**	**The child depicts limited understanding of ways to sort pebbles with overlapping characteristics.**	**The child depicts ways to sort pebbles with overlapping characteristics and shows 3 or more ways to sort them.**

In working with the pebbles in a small group, Christopher and Brooke used only the attribute of color to sort their pebbles. When questioned by their teacher, they were unable to find other ways to sort their pebbles. They were at the beginning level of understanding for this problem.

Brandon and Amber, also kindergartners, found more than three ways to sort, including "white, smooth, egg-shaped, circles, looks like candy and red." They are at the second level of understanding because they showed three or more separate ways to sort the pebbles.

Note: These children used only manipulatives in discussion with the teacher and did not record their work.

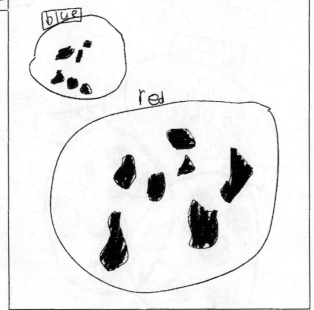

Name __Kirsten__

Pebble Sorting

Sylvester had 15 pebbles in his collection. Use pictures, diagrams and words to describe 3 or more ways he might sort his collection.

triangular   black

shine

Also at the second level is Kirsten. She showed five separate ways to sort the pebbles: triangular, black, shiny, blue and red. She did not, however, show how to depict a pebble or rock that had more than one of the characteristics.

blue

red

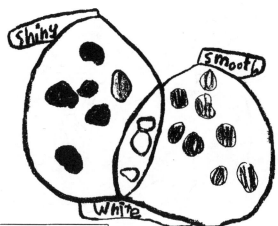

Name Sammy Ashe

Pebble Sorting

Sylvester had 15 pebbles in his collection. Use pictures, diagrams and words to describe 3 or more ways he might sort his collection.

Sammy, another first grader is at the third level. He is beginning to depict the idea that a rock may have more than one characteristic.

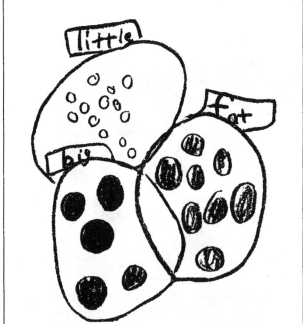

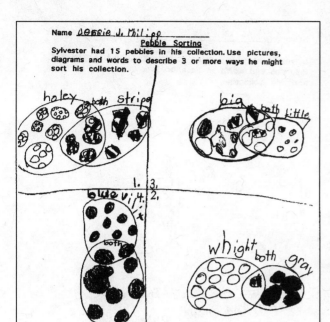

In the three examples that follow, children demonstrate a well-developed ability to consider two attributes simultaneously and represent them in words and/or pictures.

Jessie depicts 3 or more ways to sort the pebbles with overlapping characteristics. The intersection on her diagrams is labeled "both."

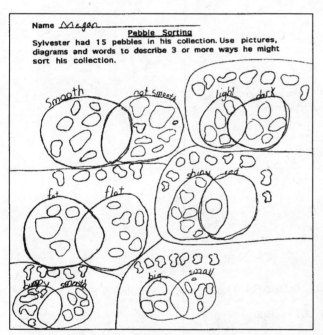

Megan finds six ways to sort the pebbles using overlapping Venn diagrams and includes all fifteen rocks each time, even when they fit outside the loops.

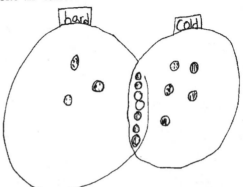

Name _Gia_

Pebble Sorting
Sylvester had 15 pebbles in his collection. Use pictures, diagrams and words to describe 3 or more ways he might sort his collection.

There are five in cold Three in hard and seven in the middle n makes 15.

In addition to labeling her intersecting diagrams, Gia describes them in sentences and includes the total number of rocks on each page.

dry has five and wet has Three and the middle has seven. Half is Dry and Half is wet.

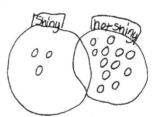

I have 12 in the not shiny and Three in shiny I have 30 all together.

If we plot the children's work on the levels of understanding, it would look like this:

Levels of Understanding

Christopher Brooke ▼	Brandon Amber Kirsten ▼	Sammy ▼	Jesse Megan Gia ▼
The child depicts less than 3 separate ways to sort the pebbles.	The child depicts 3 or more separate ways to sort the pebbles.	The child depicts limited understanding of ways to sort pebbles with overlapping characteristics.	The child depicts ways to sort pebbles with overlapping characteristics and shows 3 or more ways to sort them.

This is an activity that needs to be repeated often throughout the school year. Vary the items you use to sort. Junk or treasure boxes are good sources of things to sort. A related activity in this book is the lesson "How Many Snails?"

References

Baylor, Byrd. *Everybody Needs a Rock*. New York: Aladdin Paperbacks, 1985.

Garland, Cynthia. *Mathematics Their Way Summary Newsletter*, Saratoga, CA: Center for Innovation in Education, 1990.

Steig, William. *Sylvester and the Magic Pebble*. New York: Aladdin Paperbacks, 1987.

The Duckling Problem

Materials

- Unifix cubes or other counting materials
- *Make Way for Ducklings* by Robert McCloskey
- Unlined paper
- Pencils, crayons, and/or colored marking pens
- Overhead projector (optional)
- Screen (optional)
- Overhead transparencies of children's work (optional)
- Individual chalkboards, chalk, and erasers.

Overview

For this problem, children write or dictate a story about what might happen if some of Mr. and Mrs. Mallard's ducklings wander away. Older children are asked to write a number sentence to go with their story. Allow at least 40 minutes for the children to tell their stories about what happened to the ducklings.

Description

Begin by reading the book *Make Way for Ducklings* to the children. Ask the students to retell the story. Then tell them they are going to make up stories about what might happen if some of the ducklings wander away. For older children, write the following on the chalkboard:

> **Mr. and Mrs. Mallard had 8 ducklings. Tell a story about what might happen if some of them wander away. Draw a picture and write a number sentence to go with your story.**

As you write, tell the children about the problem. Then, brainstorm things that may have happened to some of the ducklings after they left their parents. As the children orally share ideas, you may want to model number sentences that go with their stories. For younger children, you can write the task on the board, but be sure that every child understands there were eight ducklings and some of them wandered away.

Before you dismiss the children to begin their work, be sure that they know they are to draw a picture, write a story, and show a number sentence about the ducklings that have disappeared. Kindergartners can draw their picture and then dictate the story to you or another adult. Depending on the time of year, some first grade students may need to dictate their story to an older student or an adult.

As children finish writing or dictating their problems, you may want to make overheads of some of them. Make sure that the children can read or describe their solutions.

When all the children have finished, have each child get an individual chalkboard, chalk and eraser. Then show the overheads or ask for volunteers to read their problems. Using their individual chalkboards, ask all the children to write the number sentences and solve the problems that the class has written.

If you would like to begin with an easier problem, try the following:

> **Some ducks were swimming in a pond. Some others joined them. Write a story about what happened. Include a picture and a number sentence about your story.**

Student Responses and Assessment

Kindergarten children drew pictures about the story and were interviewed by the teacher. Some children told how the ducklings got lost, but became confused when the teacher asked how many ducklings were left. Others were confused about the mathematics in the problem. For example, Monica added instead of subtracted when she said, "The mama duck was looking at the cars and the baby duck wandered away and never came back. It crossed all the streets and got runned over. Nine were left." Chris told the number of ducks who were lost but did not reveal how many remained: "They were swimming and people were throwing peanuts and a big bird pushing the boat. Five ducklings got lost." Other children knew exactly how many were left. Bonnie said, "This is when they were counting the eggs and they hatched. One little baby swam away. One left and that makes

seven." Mark drew a picture of a tiny duck being run over by a car and said, "One of the ducklings died because he didn't listen to the other ducklings. He went in the street and the cars runned over the little duckling. Seven were left."

A first and second grade class really enjoyed telling their own duckling stories. To strengthen the language arts-mathematics connection, students can brainstorm and record a list of possible things that might have happened to the ducklings that wandered off, as shown in the example below:

What Happened to the Missing Ducklings?

- a poacher took them
- they fell in the lake
- a policeman took them to the zoo
- a car ran over them
- a fox ate them
- a kid took them home
- a sea monster ate them
- they got lost when they walked through the park

The children's written work can be placed on a continuum of the following **levels of understanding:**

Levels of Understanding

▼	▼	▼	▼
The child demonstrates an understanding of the story with no reference to the mathematics involved.	The child depicts some of the basic mathematical elements of the problem.	The child depicts most of the mathematical elements of the problem, and demonstrates an understanding of subtraction.	The child demonstrates knowledge of subtraction and writes (or dictates) a number sentence to go with the problem.

Examples of the first **level of understanding**, which demonstrate an understanding of the story with no reference to the mathematics, are shown below:

Ann Marie draws a duckling and some eggs. She dictates to her teacher, "There's one duckling. I colored all the eggs white. The eggs didn't hatch yet."

Jenika draws some ducklings and paraphrased the story, "They had baby ducklings. They were going to the pond to meet their dad there. They almost got runned over by cars and the police stopped the cars."

The next examples depict some of the basic mathematical elements of the problem.

Lydia, a kindergarten child, refers to the idea of subtraction when she dictates, "Quack was looking the other way, not watching where he was going. All the other ducklings were saying, 'Quack's behind.' Seven were walking behind their mother."

Tiffany also hints at subtraction when she says, "They're walking to their home. They're going to sleep. Three went to their home. Six were walking."

Examples of the first **level of understanding**, which demonstrate an understanding of the story with no reference to the mathematics, are shown below:

Ann Marie draws a duckling and some eggs. She dictates to her teacher, "There's one duckling. I colored all the eggs white. The eggs didn't hatch yet."

Jenika draws some ducklings and paraphrased the story, "They had baby ducklings. They were going to the pond to meet their dad there. They almost got runned over by cars and the police stopped the cars."

Name Andrew H

Mr. Mallard was caching breakfast when a net fel over two. There were 6 left. 8-2=6

$$\begin{array}{r} 8 \\ -2 \\ \hline 6 \end{array}$$

At the fourth level of understanding, the child demonstrates knowledge of subtraction and writes (or dictates) a number sentence to go with the problem.

Andrew, a first grader, draws a picture of two ducklings caught in a net while Mr. Mallard was out catching breakfast. He includes an accurate equation.

Name J.J.

Msr. mallard and hur ducklings war looking for Mr. Mallard but they did't see a duck pochre the pochre cot thee of the ducklings. So they was 5 duckling left.

Bostin

J.J.'s mom is a naturalist, and he writes about a poacher who catches three of the ducklings and leaves five.

The children's work for this problem might be placed on the **levels of understanding** as follows:

Levels of Understanding

Ann Marie Jenika	Lydia Tiffany	Michael Megan	Andrew H. J. J.
▼	▼	▼	▼
The child demonstrates an understanding of the story with no reference to the mathematics involved.	The child depicts some of the basic mathematical elements of the problem.	The child depicts most of the mathematical elements of the problem, and demonstrates an understanding of subtraction.	The child demonstrates knowledge of subtraction and writes (or dictates) a number sentence to go with the problem.

This problem gives the teacher the chance to assess how comfortable children are with story problems and find out if they can use numbers to tell how many are left or if they can write an equation. The problem was posed at the beginning of the school year in kindergarten. These children were typically engrossed in telling their story, and the numbers were far less important. It is likely that a significant number of children, at this point in time, will have difficulty expressing the number of remaining ducks. In fact, the children who were able to determine the number of remaining ducks usually simplified the problem so that only one of eight ducks wandered off!

With first and second grade children, this problem was posed in the spring of the year, and the children's choice of numbers was revealing as well. Those children comfortable only with smaller numbers usually chose those numbers to use in their problem. This is the beauty of open-ended questions. They allow children to modify the problem to meet their own developmental needs. The resulting information is extremely valuable to the teacher.

Extensions

A problem such as this, which allows children to plug in their own numbers in an open-ended format, could be adapted to other areas of study. A similar problem, for instance, might be written for the book *A Bargain for Frances* by Russell Hoban.

> **Frances had fifteen cents. Tell a story about what might happen if she spent some of her money. Draw a picture and write a number sentence to go with your story.**

Another adaptation of this problem might be used around St. Patrick's Day:

> **Larry Leprechaun found 12 four-leaf clovers. Some disappeared. Tell a story about what happened. Draw a picture and write a number sentence to go with your story.**

References

McCloskey, Robert. *Make Way for Ducklings.* New York: Puffin; Pap/Com Ed., 2010.

Pattern Block Puzzles

Materials

- Pattern blocks or other geometric building materials
- *Shapes, Shapes, Shapes* by Tana Hoban
- File Folders or books to use as screens
- Chart paper labeled **Geometry Words**
- Unlined paper
- Pencils, crayons, and/or colored marking pens
- Overhead projector (optional)
- Screen (optional)
- Overhead transparencies of children's work (optional)
- Post-it notes (optional)

Overview

In this problem, children create pattern block puzzles for their classmates to solve. First, they work only with materials. Then, they record their solutions with pictures and/or words. Allow at least two extended math periods for the children to solve the problem.

Description

It is helpful to begin this lesson with a book that describes different shapes. One possible suggestion is *Shapes, Shapes, Shapes* by Tana Hoban. After you read the book, discuss how riddles or word puzzles can be used to describe shapes. Play an "I Spy" game with the children describing various geometric shapes in the classroom. (For example, "I spy a large rectangle hanging on the wall" or "I spy a small plastic rectangle near the door.")

Then tell the children that you have built a puzzle with three pattern blocks behind the screen on the overhead projector (or on a desk in the front of the room). Ask three or four volunteers to rebuild your puzzle on their desks as you present each step of your oral directions. If your puzzle looks like this,

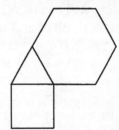

you might say: "You will need an orange square, green triangle, and yellow hexagon. (Pause). Place the orange square block closest to you on your desk. (Pause). Add a green triangle to the top of the orange square so the sides touch exactly. (Pause). On the right side of the green triangle place one side of the yellow hexagon so that the sides touch."

Add additional directions if you sense that the children need more information to complete the puzzle successfully (i.e., "Your puzzle will be flat on the table.") Show the class your puzzle (on the overhead or on the floor in front of them) and see if it matches what the children have built.

Next have the class work in partners to give verbal directions for making matching pattern block puzzles. With a screen between them, one partner gives directions to the other child for making a pattern block design with three pattern blocks. The children then switch roles so each child has the chance to practice giving clear directions. If discrepancies occur, remind children that the task requires two people to make it successful—a good describer and a good listener who can follow directions. Young children who are providing descriptions may need to watch their partners as they begin to build. Then they can modify their directions if their partner is not building the intended puzzle. This will create less frustration for both children.

When each child has had a chance to give a set of directions, call the class back together and place any three pattern block shapes next to each other on the overhead projector. Ask the children to suggest directions to create an identical puzzle. As the children provide directions, write them on the chalkboard. Then try to rebuild the puzzle using the directions the children have dictated to you.

Tell the children that the class will create a **Geometry Words** chart to help them think of and write good directions for their puzzles. Have them suggest words that might belong on the chart and add them.

On the following day, put three new pattern block pieces next to each other on the overhead projector. Have the children again describe how to rebuild this design. Write their directions on the chalkboard and use them to build a design. Revise or add to the directions as necessary. Add any new words to the **Geometry Words** chart. Be sure to include any position words such as: **next to, between, left, right, below, above**, and so on, along with geometric terms such as **hexagon, trapezoid, triangle, square, angle**, and **side**.

Tell the children that they will create their own puzzles with any three pattern blocks. First, they will build a design with the three pattern blocks. Then, they will copy their design by tracing around the blocks onto one side of their paper. On the other side of the paper, the children will write the directions for building their design so clearly that someone else could build their "puzzle" without seeing the design. (Children not yet able to write on their own may dictate the directions to an adult or older student.) Be sure to erase the directions you wrote on the chalkboard and emphasize that the puzzles the children build need to be different from the ones you did.

When most of the children are finished, read some of the students' directions and have the rest of the children attempt to build each puzzle that is described. Choose papers that are clear and that other children will be able to rebuild easily.

Student Responses and Assessment

Children respond with varying degrees of sophistication to this task. The range of responses you might expect from kindergarten, first, and second grade children looks like this:

Levels of Understanding

The child uses few or no geometric or position words to present a limited description of the placement of the blocks.	The child sometimes uses geometric and/or position words to present a partial description of the placement of the blocks.	The child consistently uses geometric and/or position words to present a complete description of the placement of the blocks.

Both Brooke and Alicia are at the **first level of understanding** for this problem.

Brooke, a kindergartner, uses no geometric or position words in her description. Her teacher wrote down her exact words: "I put one and then the other." She did not elaborate when questioned further by her teacher.

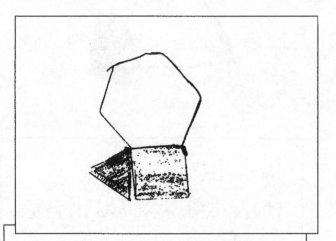

alicia
pattern bIck
puzzle PUt the
hexagon by The
Triangle & The sqre.

First grader Alicia names the shapes in her puzzle, but uses no other geometric or position words in her description.

Alison T. and Kelli are at the **second level of understanding** .

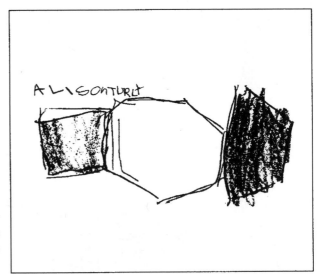

Alison uses some position and geometric terms but omits the word "hexagon". A kindergartner, she dictates to her teacher: "I put the orange square first and the yellow thing in the middle and the red trapezoid on the right side."

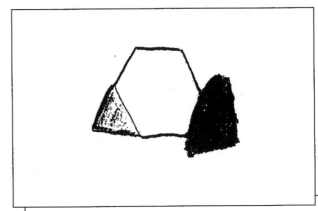

Kelli, a first grader, accurately describes a part of her design. Although she uses left and right appropriately, she does not state where the triangle or diamond are placed in relation to the hexagon. She also does not state whether the diamond is the blue or tan pattern block.

Pattern Block puzzle Kelli
it has a diamond and it has a triangle and a hexagon frist you put the hexagon in the mitoll then you put diamond on your lateft sod and then you put the triangle on your rat sod.

Alison H. and Jessie are at the **highest level of understanding**.

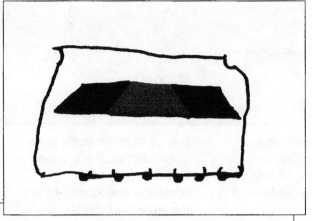

Alison

I uosed A trapezoid ANd too diamonds ANd I Trapezoid in The middle And put The diamo on The Side ANd it will LooK like A biger trapezoid

Alison's description is brief but succinct. She tells the builder what the finished product will be like.

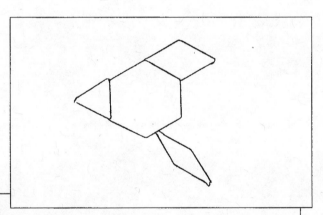

Jessie

fist you take a ◇ and putit so there is a point at the top and Bottom. Then take a △ and put it Sord of like a clowns hat exept you put it on the left middle side. Then take a Blue ◇ and make it look like a parallelogram and put it on the top right side. Then take the gray ◇ and put it Sord of slated to the right and put on the Bottom right side.

Jessie gives a very complete description and also incorporates her own experience when she writes that the triangle will look "sort of like a clown's hat."

The children's work could be placed on the levels of understanding for this problem as follows:

Levels of Understanding

Brooke **Alicia** ▼	**Alison T.** **Kelli** ▼	**Alison H.** **Jessie** ▼
The child uses few or no geometric or position words to present a limited description of the placement of the blocks.	The child sometimes uses geometric and/or position words to present a partial description of the placement of the blocks.	The child consistently uses geometric and/or position words to present a complete description of the placement of the blocks.

This is an activity that can be repeated throughout the year. The children love to create their own puzzles for other people to solve. They also take great pride in their accomplishments! They learn that there is tremendous power in mathematical communication as they see that their oral and written words can explain to someone else how to build their puzzle. To involve the children's family and friends in this learning process, display the written puzzles and have pattern blocks available at open house for everyone to solve.

References

Hoban, Tana. *Shapes, Shapes, Shapes.* New York: HarperCollins Publishers, 1996.

Unifix Trains

Materials

- Unifix cubes, colored wooden cubes, or other counting materials
- *Freight Train* by Donald Crews, *The Little Engine That Could* by Watty Piper, or *Choo Choo* by Virginia Lee Burton
- Unlined paper
- Pencils, crayons, and/or colored marking pens
- Overhead projector (optional)
- Screen (optional)
- Overhead transparencies of children's work (optional)
- Post-it notes (optional)

Overview

In this problem, children are asked to find possible combinations of three or four different colored cars for a unifix cube train. Allow at least two extended math periods for the children to solve the problem.

Description

To introduce this lesson, read a book about trains to your children. Discuss the colors of the various cars. Then present the following problem:

> **On one train, the engine is black and always goes first. The caboose is red and always goes last. The cars in the middle are green, blue, and yellow. How many different ways can you arrange the cars in the middle?**

Using unifix cubes, build a train for the children to see. Then build a second train and change the order of the middle colors. Ask the children to think of other ways to arrange the colors in the middle so they are different from the first two. Have one or two children build trains that are different than the first two. Tell the children that there are six different ways to arrange the cars in the middle of the train. Their job is to find as many as they can of the six possible ways. They may draw or use unifix cubes to represent the trains, but should find a way to keep track of the ones they already have to make sure that none are repeated. Have students share and compare solutions.

In kindergarten, this problem is already a challenge. Older children can work with this problem on the first day of the lesson. Then, they can explore the following more difficult problem on the second day:

> **On another train, the engine is also black and always goes first. The caboose is red and always goes last. The cars in the middle are green, blue, yellow and orange. How many different ways can you arrange the cars in the middle?**

Before they attempt to solve this problem, review some of the children's work from the first lesson with three middle cars. Discuss the various methods that children used to organize their solutions. Ask children to predict the number of ways that four cars could be arranged in the middle of the train. Then challenge them to find out as many as possible or even all of the combinations of the cars. To help children focus on a reasonable number of combinations, you may want to tell them that there are more than twenty but fewer than thirty different ways to arrange the cars. One teacher narrowed the range further when she revealed that the number was over twenty and under twentyfive.

The goal of this lesson is to encourage children to look to themselves for a sense of completion in an open-ended project. As children explore this problem, urge them to check for duplicates and also search for patterns in their solutions. Ask them how they **know** they have all the combinations, but be satisfied if a child is content when over twenty are found.

Discuss the children's answers, and encourage them to share their thoughts. If you choose to use overheads of student work, try to choose some samples that show some kind of organization or planning (i.e., all of the combinations with blue first, then all with green first...). If you have previously presented the Crazy Mixed-Up Animal problem, you may want to ask the children to compare how these problems are similar and different. [Teachers note: In Crazy Mixed-Up Animals the order of the animals does make a difference (heads need to come before bodies), therefore the activity is a defined as a mathematical combination. In contrast, the cars between the engine and the caboose in the Unifix Trains can be arranged in any order, therefore this activity is a permutation It is not important that the students know the vocabulary, but you may want to help them see the differences in the two types of problems.]

Student Responses and Assessment:

Kindergarten children worked with the first problem where six was the total number of different arrangements of cars on the train. The kindergartners worked in small groups with their teacher. She kept a written record of each child's solution as well as their comments. There are twenty-four possible arrangements for the second problem for first and second grade children. These older children drew and/or wrote about their responses.

The student responses in both kindergarten and in first and second grades follow similar levels of understanding:

Levels of Understanding

▼	▼	▼	▼
The child depicts half or fewer than half of the possible arrangements of train cars.	The child depicts more than half of the possible arrangements of train cars. Some of the combinations may be duplicated.	The child represents all or almost all of the arrangements of train cars without duplications in a guess and check or random fashion.	The child represents all or almost all of the arrangements of train cars without duplications in an organized and systematic fashion.

Sarah and Patrick illustrate the most basic level of understanding. Sarah, a kindergartner, found three ways to arrange the trains. According to her teacher's observations and notes, Sarah said, "Mrs. Thomas, I can't think of any more." Patrick, a first grader whose work is shown, depicted fewer than half of the twenty-four combinations.

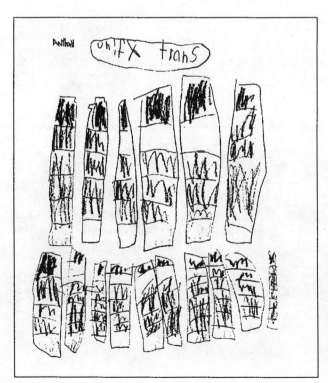

Josh and Anthony are the second level of understanding. Josh, a kindergartner, found four of the possible combinations, according to his teacher's report. Anthony, a first grader, drew fifteen out of the 24 possible combinations, as shown to the left. Some of his combinations were duplicated.

Mark and Katie are at the third level of understanding. Mark randomly found five of the six possible combinations, and reported to his kindergarten teacher, "I'm going to draw one when I get home." Katie, a second grader whose work is shown to the right, found a total of 24 combinations in a random fashion.

Breann, Michael and Megan are at the highest level of understanding, though their approaches to the problem are quite diverse. Breann, a kindergartner, found all six ways to represent the combinations and tried to use patterns to help her. She told her teacher, "It looks like a quilt." Michael, a second grader, found all twenty-four ways to represent the combinations. His work, shown to the left, depicts the systematic pattern used to find his solution.

Megan

unifix trains

We got 23 unifix trains first we got 25 but we foud out that we had sames the ancer has to be 23 because we only had two doblicates and we can't find any more. Mrs myren Said it is over 20 and under 25.

13	14	15	16	17	18	19	20	21	22	23
black	black	black	black	black	black	black	black	black	black	black
yellow	orange	orange	orange	green	green	green	orange	green	green	green
orange	blue	blue	green	orange	orange	blue	yellow	yellow	blue	yellow
blue	green	yellow	yellow	yellow	blue	orange	green	blue	yellow	orange
green	yellow	green	blue	blue	yellow	yellow	blue	orange	orange	blue
red	red	red	red	red	red	red	red	red	red	red

1	2	3	4	5	6	7	8	9	10	11	12
black	black	black	black	black	black	black	black	black	black	black	black
blue	blue	blue	blue	blue	blue	blue	orange	yellow	yellow	yellow	yellow
yellow	green	orang	yellow	green	yellow	orange	yellow	blue	blue	orange	green
orange	orange	yellow	green	yellow	orange	green	blue	green	orange	green	blue
green	yellow	green	orange	orange	green	yellow	green	orange	green	blue	orange
red	red	red	red	red	red	red	red	red	red	red	red

Megan found 23 out of the 24 combinations and organized her work in a very logical fashion.

These children would fit on the levels of understanding as follows:

Levels of Understanding

Sarah, Patrick	Josh, Anthony	Mark, Katie	Breann, Michael, Megan
The child depicts half or fewer than half of the possible arrangements of train cars.	The child depicts more than half of the possible arrangements of train cars. Some of the combinations may be duplicated.	The child represents all or almost all of the arrangements of train cars without duplications in a guess and check or random fashion.	The child represents all or almost all of the arrangements of train cars without duplications in an organized and systematic fashion.

This problem can be revisited in a number of ways. You may want to try having children show all the different ways three or four scoops of ice cream can be arranged on a cone, as in the following problem:

> At the ice cream shop you order a scoop of chocolate, a scoop of strawberry, and a scoop of vanilla on your ice cream cone. How many ways might the ice cream cone be arranged? What would happen if you added a scoop of lemon?

Another idea is to find possible ways to organize the lineup for a pet parade:

> There are four pets in the neighborhood pet parade. A rabbit, a cat, a goat and a dog. How many different ways can all four animals line up for the parade?

References

Burton, Virginia Lee. *Choo Choo*. New York: Houghton Mifflin Harcourt, 1988.

Crews, Donald. *Freight Train*. New York: Greenwillow Books, 1992.

Piper, Watty. *The Little Engine That Could*. New York: Grosset & Dunlap, 1991

Measuring Neil's Desk

Materials

- Unifix cubes, paper clips, and crayons
- Unlined paper
- Pencils, crayons, and/or colored marking pens
- Overhead projector (optional)
- Screen (optional)
- Overhead transparencies of children's work (optional)

Overview

In this problem, children are asked to find out what happens when they measure a desk with various sized-objects. They are asked to tell what happens to the numbers when the size of the object changes.

Description

Ask the children if they can estimate the size of their desks if they measured it with unifix cubes. Then ask them if they think the number would change if they used crayons to measure it. For older children, write the following on the chalkboard:

> **Neil (use the name of a child in your class) measured his classroom desk. First he used large paper clips. Then he used unifix cubes. Last he tried his new crayons. He got different numbers each time. Estimate the desk's measurements with each object and explain why the numbers are different.**

As you write, tell the children about the problem. As a group brainstorm ways they might find the answer. For younger children, simply read the problem to them. Make sure every child knows what his/her task is.

Simplify the task for kindergarten children. Their problem is:

> **Neil (use the name of a child in your class) measured his desk. First he used unifix cubes. Then he used his new crayons. He got different numbers each time. Try measuring your desk with unifix cubes and then crayons. Did you get different numbers? Why do you think the numbers are different?**

Before you dismiss the children to begin their work, be sure that they know they are to draw a picture, write, and/or dictate to an adult the results of their measuring. With kindergarten children, have them draw their picture and then have them dictate the results to you or another adult. Depending on the time of year, some first grade students also may need to dictate to an older student or an adult.

As children finish writing or dictating their results, you may want to make overhead transparencies of some of their solutions. Then, have those children share their solutions with the class. If you are working with kindergarten children, you may want to have the children share their results in the small groups when all the children have finished.

A book that may help introduce the idea of using nonstandard objects for measurement is *The Line Up Book* by Marisabina Russo. In this story, a young boy is called for lunch by his mother while he is lining up objects from his room throughout the house. Each time he runs out of an object (books, toy trucks, blocks), he changes to another form of measurement.

Student Responses and Assessment

In most kindergarten classes, the children work at large tables rather than individual desks. In one classroom, the teacher had the children use chalkboards to simulate Neil's desk top. The children in this same class also decided to try different items to measure in addition to the unifix cubes and crayons. As they worked with the teacher in small groups, she was able to observe the different techniques the children used to count and measure the chalkboards. The children dictated their responses to the teacher. Interestingly, the children all chose to measure the entire distance **around** the chalkboards, rather than the length, width or surface area.

In a first and second grade classroom, the children decided that they would personalize the problem by putting their name in the title. So Jessie, for example, renamed the problem "Measuring Jessie's Desk." These students chose to use linear measurements of the length, width or perimeter of the desk.

In kindergarten through second grades, the children's response to this problem could be grouped into the following levels of understanding:

Levels of Understanding

▼	▼	▼
The child attempts to measure the desk, but does not use materials to compare and/or depict the results.	The child uses the materials to measure the desk and reports the amount for each item but does not account for differences in measurements.	The child measures the desk, compares the numbers and makes a generalization that the number of items is related to the size of the item.

Neil
Measuring Neil's Desk

I think it is 16 inches
and my estimate
11 inches.

Lillian, a kindergarten child, used only pattern blocks and did not measure and compare them with a second item. When interviewed by her teacher, she stated there were 28 pattern blocks. She is at the **first level of understanding**.

Developmentally, this is a challenging problem for many kindergarten and first graders. Neil had difficulty understanding the task and measured his desk in inches. He is at the first level of understanding because he did not use the materials specified in the problem.

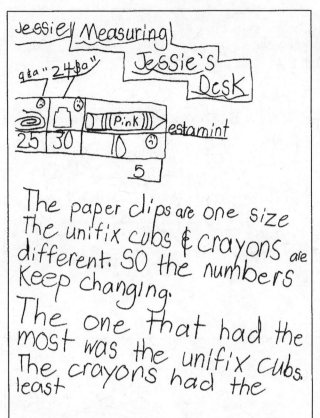

The paper clips are one size
The unifix cubs & crayons are
different. SO the numbers
Keep changing.
The one that had the
most was the unifix cubs.
The crayons had the
least

Another kindergarten child, Erika, used green pattern blocks and then crayons to measure. She placed 31 pattern blocks around the board, and then used 10 crayons to measure the same distance. Her comment to her teacher was, "It took more pattern blocks." She is at the **second level of understanding** because she used two different materials to compare and told her teacher the amount for each one. Jessie and Joseph, in the examples that follow, are also on the **second level of understanding**.

Jessie showed her estimate and the actual amount. Note the sad faces, indicating that she was unhappy with her estimates. She did not generalize that the longer the item used to measure, the less of that item it would take, so she is on the second level of understanding.

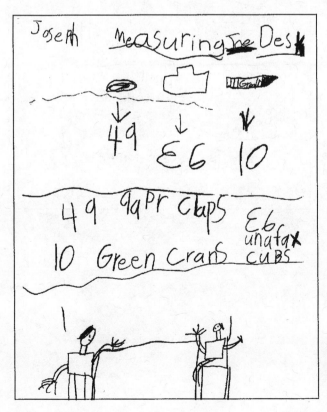

Joseph, a first grader, is also at the second level. He measured his desk with each item, but did not reach a generalization about the sizes.

Jayme, a kindergarten child, measured around her board with ten crayons. She next started to use the unifix cubes. When she had placed only ten unifix cubes, Jayme commented to her teacher that they already measured a shorter distance than the crayons. She finished this measurement with 50 unifix cubes, and generalized about her measurements when she said, "There are more unifix cubes because they're littler than the crayons." Jayme's work, and that of the next two children show evidence of generalizations between the size of the object used to measure and the number it took. They are at the **third level of understanding** for this problem.

Russell compares the size of the paper clip and the unifix cube to the size of the crayon. This second grader realizes that the larger the item, the fewer it takes to complete the measurement.

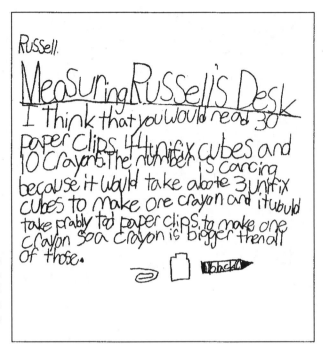

Eric, a first grader, states that, "The littler (the items used to measure) the more. The bigger (the items used to measure) the less."

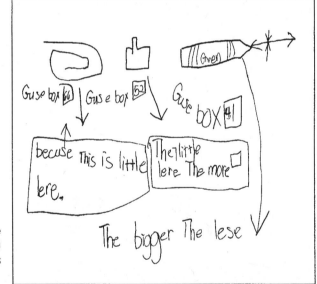

▲▼▲

Here is how the work of these children would be placed
on the levels of understanding for this problem:

Levels of Understanding

Lillian Neil ▼	Erika Jessie Joseph ▼	Jayme Russell Eric ▼
The child attempts to measure the desk, but does not use materials to compare and/or depict the results.	The child uses the materials to measure the desk and reports the amount for each item but does not account for differences in measurements.	The child measures the desk, compares the numbers and makes a generalization that the number of items is related to the size of the item.

This problem was presented so that children could
select what aspects of the desk to measure (length,
width, perimeter, surface area). As illustrated
below, Joel decided to measure the desk in two
ways — from top to bottom and from side to side.
Had the problem directed Joel to measure in one
particular way (i.e., lengthwise), the teacher would
not have seen his ability to generate multiple
aspects to measure the desk. This is the value of
open-ended questions!

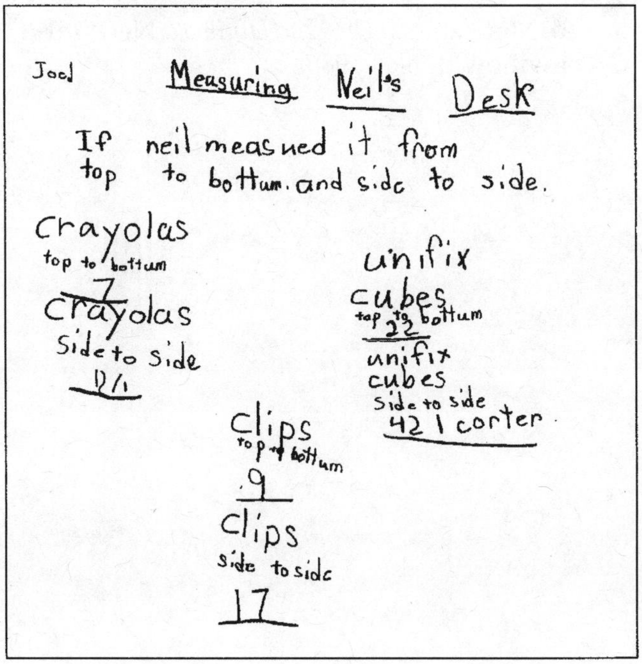

Joel

Measuring Neil's Desk

If neil measned it from
top to bottum. and side to side.

Crayolas
top to bottum
7

Crayolas
side to side
11

unifix
cubes
top to bottum
22

unifix
cubes
side to side
42 1 corter.

clips
top to bottum
9

clips
side to side
17

Joel's work is not on the levels of
understanding continuum. His
work is shown as an example of a
creative student who expresses
much knowledge.

Another important aspect of this lesson was illustrated by Jessie's work. Jessie was disappointed when her estimate did not match the actual number. It is natural that young children will attempt to change their estimates to match the actual number so they can get the "right" answer. Be sure to let the children know that you are not concerned that the estimate is correct. You may want to tell them that an estimate is only a guess, and can sometimes help us express our thinking. The more information we have, the closer our guess will become.

The expectations for solving this problem vary with the age and experience of the child. Younger children often worked with the measurement task and were only able to say which tool resulted in the largest measurement. Older children were able to state which measurement tool produced the lowest and highest numbers, and also could be specific about exact measurements for the desk. Many of the oldest children were able to make the generalization that longer measuring tools resulted in smaller numbers, and smaller tools produced larger numbers.

Extensions

For assessment purposes, keep in mind that young children may require several experiences with an idea or concept before they can internalize it and apply it in their own framework. The children need to have several measurement lessons before they can make generalizations. To provide children with additional measurement experiences with nonstandard objects of different lengths, the following problem can be used:

Katie measured herself (with a friend helping her). First she used toothpicks. Then she used wooden cubes. Last she used pencils. Estimate the number she may have counted for each object. Explain why the numbers are different.

Another problem suitable for older children connects this activity to standard measurement:

You want to measure the length of the chalkboard in your classroom and the length of your reading book. You may use inches, feet, or yards. Which would you choose to measure each item and why?

References

Russo, Marisabina. *The Line Up Book*. New York: Greenwillow Books, 1986.

Read-A-Graph

Materials

- Chart paper or butcher paper
- One 3" square paper per child
- Glue stick
- A graph to read—one that the class has generated or the animal graph on page 112 of this book.
- Unlined paper
- Pencils, crayons, and/or colored marking pens
- Overhead projector (optional)
- Screen (optional)
- Overhead transparencies of children's work (optional)

Overview

Children interpret a graph—either one that the class generates or one that they are given. Allow at least 40 minutes for the children to draw, write and/or dictate their interpretations. Plan on additional time if the graph itself needs to be generated.

Description

With first and second grade children, have the children interpret class graphs first, and then present the open-ended animal graph. With kindergarten children, have the class do a graph together, and then have them interpret the results.

To make a class graph to interpret, have 3" squares of white paper cut for the children. You also may want to have the question written on chart paper or butcher paper. The question you choose can relate to a current unit of study. Some possible questions that make interesting graphs are:

> **How many people live with you?**
> **What pets do you have?**
> **What is your favorite food for (a particular holiday) dinner?**
> **What kind of shoes are you wearing?**
> **What is your favorite color?**

To make sure that children are free to express their own ideas with questions that deal with opinions or "favorites," have them commit to their answer before the graph is assembled. To assure this, the children can whisper their choices to a neighbor; once a choice is verbalized children are less likely to change their selection to a more popular column. Or, the children can draw their choices on blank squares of paper before the group graph is made.

Note that not all the questions deal with "favorites." Young children need to know that graphing is not always a popularity contest, so be sure to include graphing that deal with factual knowledge, such as, **How many aunts (or uncles) do you have?**

After you have written the question on the large paper, you may want to fold it and list the categories. Or, you can have the children generate the categories. A shoe graph might look like this:

What kind of shoes are you wearing?		
laces	velcro	buckles

The question may be written on the top or bottom of the graph. Because you want the children to interpret given data, the organization for this graph can come from you. (In contrast, the activity **Safari Toss/ Color Toss** asks children to organize their own data.) The main objective in this lesson is to help children **interpret** data.

After you have made the graph, gather the children together and pose the question. Then ask each child to draw his or her response on a paper square. (Squares are ideal because they can be rotated and still maintain the same shape; this way, children's responses will all be right-side up!) Then have the children use glue sticks to place their responses in the proper columns. After the graph is complete, discuss together the results and what they might mean. Next, have older children write their ideas about the graph, while younger ones dictate their thoughts to you or another person.

After your children have become fairly proficient at interpreting their own graphs, try giving them the open-ended animal graph to interpret. This graph has no title and the columns are only identified with an animal picture:

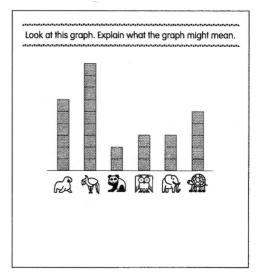

Look at this graph. Explain what the graph might mean.

The animal graph has no title and the vertical and horizontal axes of the graph are not labeled. The interpretations of the children will vary. In first grade, you may want to begin this activity as a whole group and brainstorm a list of the children's possible solutions. In second grade, it is appropriate to have the children write about the possibilities.

This graph can be revisited later in the year if you substitute other pictures on the horizontal axis. For example, a graph with pictures of food, might suggest different interpretations.

Student Responses and Assessment

The following levels of understanding were found in the range of student work from Grades K-2:

Levels of Understanding

▼ The child presents a basic description of the graph and uses few or no comparison words or mathematical terms to interpret the data.

▼ The child presents a partial description of the graph and sometimes uses comparison words and/or mathematical terms to interpret the data.

▼ The child presents a complete description of the graph and consistently uses comparison words and/or mathematical terms to interpret the data.

Kindergarten

Kindergartners enjoy creating and then interpreting their own graphs. Many times, a total group discussion follows and the teacher solicits selected input about what a child knows. To insure that every child has an opportunity to respond to a graph, one kindergarten teacher interviews her children three or four times a year about a class generated graph. She began one year at Thanksgiving, and interviewed the children about a Thanksgiving Favorites graph.

When asked about the graph, Matt, Lydia, and Michael demonstrated the most **basic level of understanding** because they use few or no mathematical terms or comparison words. In a typical response, Matt focused only on the column with the most when he said, "They like the turkey. I only like the turkey, too. Usually I like lots of turkey." Lydia, also mentioned turkey as the favorite: "Some people like different things. Some lines are longer than others. Turkey was our favorite dinner." Michael was fascinated with the making of the graph: "We learned how to make graphs. We can tell what the favorites are. Turkeys...there's a lot of the pictures. I think it's a good graph."

Robbie began to compare numbers when he said, "Some people did pies. Most people did turkeys. One person made cereal. Two people made mashed potatoes. One person made watermelon. Three people liked carrots." Robbie is at the **second level of understanding** because he tells about the graph using limited comparing words and/or mathematical terms.

Using the terms **more**, **less**, and **the same**, Jayme described her class graph, "There's a lot of turkeys. The pies are less than the turkeys. There's less watermelon that the pies. The broccoli is the same as the watermelon. The carrots are more than the cereal. The chicken is more than the milk." Jayme's dictation is at the **third level of understanding**.

Grades 1 & 2

In first and second grade, the children may need additional experiences similar to the kindergarten before they are able to generate possible meanings for an open-ended graph. The teacher used the following questions from *Mathematics Their Way* to encourage children to make a mathematical interpretation of class-generated graphs:

- Which column has the least?
- Which column has the most?
- Ar e there more _____ or more _____?
- Ar e there less _____ or less_____?
- How many _____ are there?
- How many mor e _____ are there than _____?
- How many less _____ are there than _____?
- How many _____ are there altogether?
- Are any columns the same?

As the children answered these questions, the teacher wrote their responses in a chart story that was then placed next to the graph. Eventually the children were able to make statements about the graph without prompting from the teacher.

In response to the open-ended animal graph, children in this same first and second grade classes gave the following possible interpretations:

Maybe it's how old they are.
It might mean how many of those animals are left in the world.
Maybe it's how far away the animals live.
It might tell how many babies they have.
Maybe it tells how many brothers they have.
Or maybe it's how many of each animal live in the L.A. Zoo.

After generating ideas from the entire class, each child was then asked to express their thoughts on paper, and explain their ideas more completely.

Richie felt the graph told how many animals were left in the wild and stated the total. His work illustrates the second level of understanding because he uses a few comparing words and/or mathematical terms to interpret the graph.

Mayra felt that the graph told the ages of the animals and then talked about the oldest and the youngest animals. Because she used more comparison words and mathematical terms, her work is on the third level of understanding.

▲▼▲

If we were to plot the levels of understanding for these kindergarten, first and second grade children, it would look like this:

Levels of Understanding

Michael
Lydia
Matt
▼

The child presents a basic description of the graph and uses few or no comparison words or mathematical terms to interpret the data.

Richie
Robbie
▼

The child presents a partial description of the graph and sometimes uses comparison words and/or mathematical terms to interpret the data.

Mayra
Jayme
▼

The child presents a complete description of the graph and consistently uses comparison words and/or mathematical terms to interpret the data.

Children need many opportunities to interpret graphs. To assess their progress in interpreting them, they need numerous chances to talk and discuss either in the whole group or in small groups. The ideas the class listed for the animal graph are all plausible. What the children need to do now is express their ideas more fully.

Children also need to be able to use mathematical terms when talking about graphs. Look for evidence of the following as they interpret class or individual graphs:

- Can the child state which column has the most? which has the least?
- Does the child use mathematical terms such as more, less, the same when comparing columns on the graph?
- Can the child formulate and solve addition and/or subtraction problems using the information on the graph?
- Does the child count and use numbers clearly to express amounts?
- Is the child able to tell why or to whom such a graph might be important?

Teachers may wish to maintain a "Graphing Words" word bank and brainstorm a list of words that are used to describe graphs (i.e., more than,

less than, equal). Students can use the word bank as they interpret graphs.

As students interpret the blank graphs, the teacher may wish to note whether any child puts a title on the graph and/or labels the horizontal and vertical axes. This is a next step for this class.

References

Baratta-Lorton, Mary. *Mathematics Their Way*. Menlo Park: Addison-Wesley, 1976.

Look at this graph. Explain what the graph might mean.

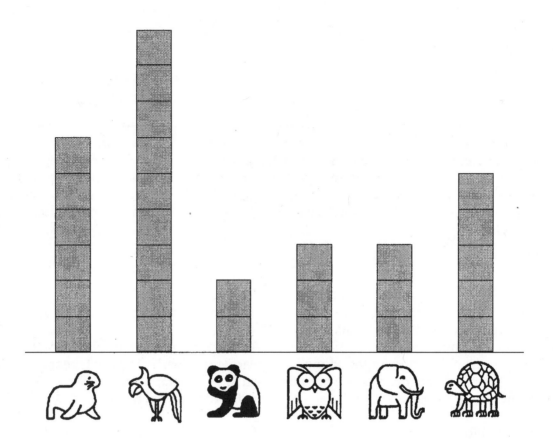

Geoboard Geometry

Materials

- Geoboards (one per student)
- Rubberbands (three per student)
- Unlined paper
- Pencils, crayons, and/or colored marking pens
- Classroom chart entitled **Geometry Words**
- Blackline masters of geoboard dot paper (optional)
- Overhead projector (optional)
- Screen (optional)
- Overhead transparencies of children's work (optional)

Overview

Children create a design or picture on a geoboard. After they reproduce this design onto paper, they tell about their creation in a written or oral report. Allow forty-five to sixty minutes for this lesson.

Description

For this activity, the children each need to have their own geoboard and three (or more) rubber bands. The number of rubber bands may be increased as the children improve their ability to record their designs. This activity should be repeated several times throughout the year to show the progress the children make in spatial visualization and writing about geometry.

Before the children work with the geoboards, remind them about your classroom safety rules. Tell them that they will be using the rubber bands to make a design or picture on their geoboard. Then, they will draw and write about their design. Ask them to imagine what their design might look like and the words they may need later to describe it. Post the Geometry Words chart and record the children's words.

After all the children understand their task, dismiss them a few at a time to get their materials and begin to explore designs on their geoboards. Generally, you should expect children to explore for at least ten to fifteen minutes before you ask them to write. When the children are ready to record their creations, you may want them to tell you the first sentence they plan to write. Remind them that they are to explain and draw what they have discovered and explored.

At the end of the lesson, share the children's work. Be sure to spend time to look at the various ways children chose to record their geoboard exploration. You also may want to add words that the children used in their writing to the **Geometry Words** chart. Use this time to build geometry vocabulary as the children use mathematical terminology in their descriptions.

There is a blackline master for geoboard dot paper on page 121 to record geoboard designs. You may decide not to use it, and instead see how the children decide to record their work on plain paper. If children are not given geoboard dot paper, you can often get a better grasp of their visual-spatial orientation. The examples shown in the following student responses are done without the geoboard dot paper.

Student Responses and Assessment

This task can be assessed on two levels—how accurately the child represents the geoboard design (Geoboard Representation), and how well the child incorporates mathematical vocabulary in the description of the design (Geoboard Report).

Geoboard Representation

Expect a wide range of responses when children copy geoboard designs. Remember that it takes a great deal of effort and concentration to produce a drawing that remotely approximates a geoboard design! Understandably, most kindergarten children ignore the nails entirely when they draw their picture. The **levels of understanding** you might expect for drawing their geoboard pictures are (from the most basic to the highest level):

Geoboard Representation Levels of Understanding

▼	▼	▼	▼
The child depicts the features of the geoboard design and eliminates all nails.	The child depicts the features of the design and shows a random number of nails on the geoboard.	The child depicts the features of the design and shows an accurate number of nails in a five by five array. However, the design is inaccurately positioned in relation to the nails.	The child depicts the features of the design and shows an accurate number of nails in a 5 x 5 array, with an accurate positioning of the design in relation to the nails.

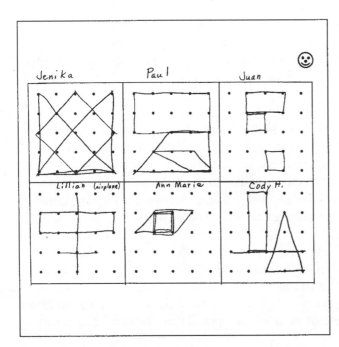

To determine the degree of accuracy, one teacher used small geoboard dot paper to quickly copy each child's design for later reference. Another teacher used Post-it notes on a clipboard to record inaccuracies as the students copied the design and later attached them to each child's work.

The following kindergarten work illustrates how the children represented the geoboard design by drawing it. The teacher worked in small groups of six to eight children and kept track of the children's designs on small dot paper (included for your use on page 122). She chose not to have the children dictate at that time because drawing their work was enough of a challenge for them. A sample of this teacher's recording is shown here.

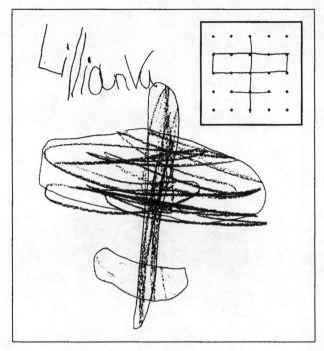

As she worked with the children, it became evident that the majority of kindergarten children ignored the geoboard nails and worked on copying shapes. Two kindergarten examples of the first level of understanding follow (with the teacher's drawings also included):

Lillian's airplane accurately depicts her geoboard creation, but ignores the placement of the nails.

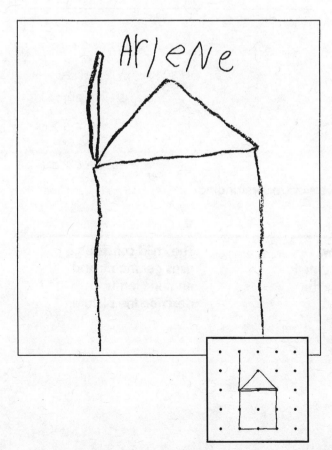

Arlene also accurately depicts her geoboard house without including the nails.

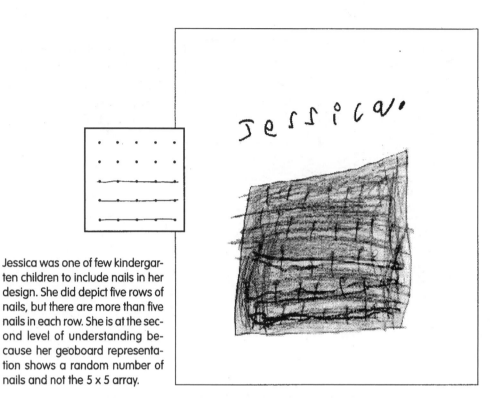

Jessica was one of few kindergarten children to include nails in her design. She did depict five rows of nails, but there are more than five nails in each row. She is at the second level of understanding because her geoboard representation shows a random number of nails and not the 5 x 5 array.

Geoboard Report

The children's oral or written reports can be assessed with the following level of understanding:

Geoboard Report Levels of Understanding

▼	▼	▼
The child uses no geometric or numeric terms to describe the picture.	The child uses few geometric and numeric terms to describe the picture.	The child consistently uses geometric and numeric terms to describe the picture.

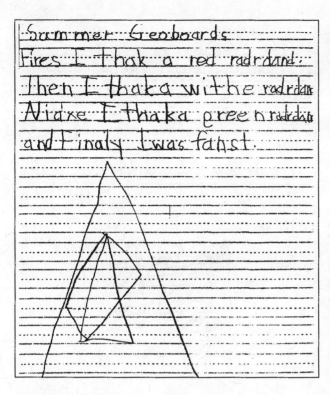

Summer Geoboards
Fires I thak a red radrdand
then I thaka wi the radrdan
Niaxe I thaka preen radrdan
and finaly I was fanst.

The following student work from first and second grade will be assessed in terms of both the **geoboard representation** and the **geoboard report**. It is evident that primary grade children can be on one level in terms of their ability to draw their geoboard and on another level with regards to their explanation.

Summer's drawing accurately shows the shapes she created without regard to the nails on the geoboard. In writing her story, she highlights the color of the rubber bands, but uses no mathematical terms. Her drawing and written response show a child at the first level of understanding in both areas.

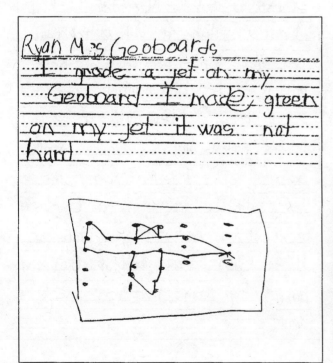

Ryan M's Geoboards
I grade a jet on my
Geoboard I made green
on my jet it was not
hard

Ryan's drawing of the geoboard is fairly complex, as he outlines the jet accurately on a 5 x 5 array. Nails are included and each of the lines representing a rubber band is purposefully related to the position of those nails. His geoboard representation is on the highest level of understanding. While his drawing is complex, his geoboard report is at the first level.

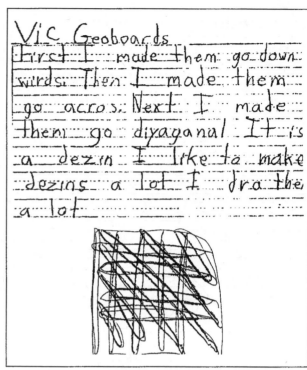

Vic's geoboard representation and report are at the second level of understanding. He depicts his design fairly accurately, but shows a random number of nails. His writing accurately describes the placement of the rubber bands by using his own position words for vertical, horizontal, and diagonal.

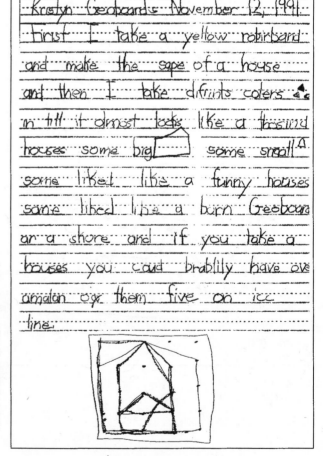

Kristyn creates an accurate representation of the nails on her geoboard, but displays some inaccuracies in the placement of the rubber bands on the drawing, characteristic of the third level of understanding. Although she was asked by the teacher to recheck her design, Kristyn was unable to detect her errors. Her report is at the first level of understanding, and describes what she made without use of mathematical terms.

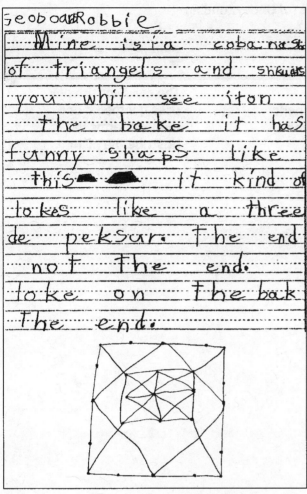

geoboard Robbie
Mine is a coba nast
of triangel's and shrus
you whil see iton
the bake it has
funny shaps like
this ▬ ▲ it kind of
tokes like a three
de peksar. The end
not the end.
toke on the bak
The end.

Robbie's drawing and writing are quite sophisticated. His work shows his ability to combine and separate shapes from a whole. He has also been able to determine the midpoints of the geoboard to reproduce his design. In both his geoboard representation and in his report, Robbie shows the highest level of understanding.

If we were to place these children on the levels of understanding for both the geoboard representation and the report, it would look like this:

Geoboard Representation Levels of Understanding

Arlene
Lillian
Summer
▼

Jessica
Vic
▼

Kristyn
▼

Ryan
Robbie
▼

The child depicts the features of the geoboard design and eliminates all nails.	**The child depicts the features of the design and shows a random number of nails on the geoboard.**	**The child depicts the features of the design and shows an accurate number of nails in a 5 x 5 array. However, the design is inaccurately positioned in relation to the nails.**	**The child depicts the features of the design and shows an accurate number of nails in a five by five array, with an accurate positioning of the design in relation to the nails.**

▲▼

Geoboard Report Levels of Understanding

Summer
Ryan
Kristyn
▼

Vic
▼

Robbie
▼

The child uses no geometric or numeric terms to describe the picture.

The child uses few geometric and numeric terms to describe the picture.

The child consistently uses geometric and numeric terms to describe the picture.

This activity should be repeated several times throughout the school year, with a goal to move the children to higher levels of understanding in both areas. Class discussions are an important tool to achieve this goal. The vocabulary building that occurs naturally is invaluable. For instance, when Vic shared his report with the class, he talked about lines that went "downwirds," across, and "diyaganul." The teacher took advantage of his description and introduced the vertical, horizontal, and diagonal to the whole class. On another occasion, Robbie reported about his design and said that it had "funny shapes," which were identified as trapezoids during the class discussion. These new words were all added to the Geometry Words chart and were mobilized by children for future descriptions

A good source for other classroom activities with geoboards that will extend children's geometry concepts is *Stretch It!* by Anne Linehan.

References

Linehan, Anne. *Stretch It! Creative Geoboard Tasks for Developing Mathematical Teaching.* San Leandro, CA: Watten/Poe Teaching Resource Center, 1992.

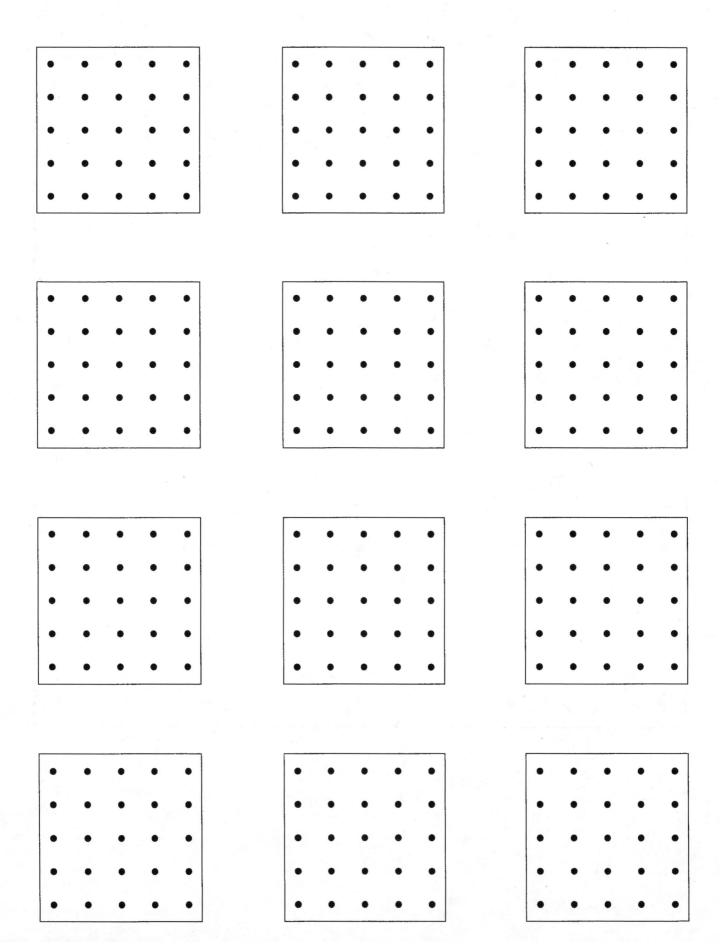

Sweet Treats

Materials

- *The M&M's Counting Book* by Barbara Barbieri McGrath

- One small, snack-sized bag of M&M's, Skittles, candy hearts or other sweets for every two children
  Note: If you would prefer not to use candy, you can substitute Unifix cubes or colored cubes.

- Small plastic bags to hold the candy after the package has been opened

- Unifix cubes, colored wooden cubes, or other counting materials

- Unlined paper

- Pencils, crayons, and/or colored marking pens

- Overhead projector (optional)

- Screen (optional)

- Overhead transparencies of children's work (optional)

- Post-it notes (optional)

Overview

In this problem, children estimate, count, and explore amounts of various small candies such as M & M's or Skittles. This is an activity that can be repeated several times throughout the year using different materials to count and explore each time. Set aside at least two extended math periods for the children to work on this problem. If possible, allow the children to generate the math problems to solve. Because this activity is student-generated, the teacher's anecdotal reports are an essential component for assessment of children's responses.

Description

Begin by reading *The M&M's Counting Book* by Barbara Barbieri McGrath to the children. This book contains activities that are appropriate for children to do with M&M's, such as sorting, counting, making shapes, adding and finally subtracting by eating them. This book is an excellent one to use if you would like the children to construct their own math explorations.

After you read the book, have the children suggest activities from the book for the class to try. This book is an excellent one to use if you would like the children to construct their own math explorations. Have at least one snack size bag of candy available for each pair of children. Note: If you would prefer not to use candy in your classroom, give each child a small bag of unifix cubes or colored cubes.

List the children's ideas about what to do with the candy (or objects). There are some interesting problems that occur if the children decide to match the number and color of their M & M's with those in the book. If possible, allow ample time for children to explore their ideas and write about their solutions.

If the book is not available, you can still have the children use a bag of candy or objects to count and compare the number of each color and the total number of items in each small bag. The children can also decide as a class the kinds of math activities that they may want to pursue.

With or without the book, pose the question: **What math can we do with the bags of candy (or objects)?** Have chart paper ready with the heading **Things to Do With _____** and ask the children to generate possible explorations.

One kindergarten class suggested the following ideas:

> **Things to do with M&M's**
>
> • **Count them**
> • **Make rainbows with them**
> • **Put them into shapes**
> • **Sort them by colors**
> • **Count each color**
> • **Draw how many of each color**
> • **Eat them by colors**
> • **Make them into cookies**
> • **Make a picture out of them**

As the children brainstorm activities, be sure to record all of their ideas; then, agree upon a method for exploration. You can choose 3 or 4 activities from the list for the children to try, or you may wish to try or attempt to try each suggestion on the list.

As you explore the activities suggested by the children, you may wish to limit the activities to one or two per day. Introduce each lesson using the **Things to Do With** _____ chart. After the topics or ideas for the day are chosen, ask the children to generate a list of the materials they'll need and brainstorm methods to proceed with the activity. For instance, one kindergarten class decided to make rainbows and determined that they needed the following items:

- paper to put the rainbows on
- paper to draw the rainbows
- M & M's
- crayons

The procedure generated by the children was to open the package of M & M's and place them on the working space paper in a rainbow fashion. Then they used the crayons and the other piece of paper to draw their arrangement.

After the children have explored one activity, use the same procedure for subsequent lessons.

Student Responses and Assessment

Some of the student-generated activities lend themselves to levels of understanding, while others can be assessed in a whole group manner. For instance, creating rainbows was actually an unexpected challenge for many of the children. They soon discovered that they needed to use the color that has the largest amount for the outside layer of the arc and the smallest number for the inside. This was an interesting application that showed if the children could order objects from smallest to largest. The size and colors of the rainbows varied according to the colors of candy in each individual bag. Often, the children's completed work looked something like this:

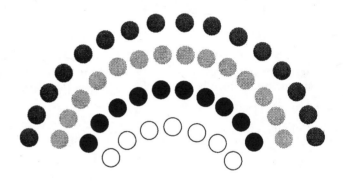

The children's written work did not lend itself to a variety of representations because they all drew the appropriate number and color of circles in arcs on their paper. However, the teacher wrote anecdotal records of how the children solved this problem on their own.

In another kindergarten class, the children wanted to count the number of candies in each package. The children decided to sort and count the candies by color. It was at the beginning of the school year in late October and the teacher asked the children to record their findings.

The children's recorded work illustrates the following levels of understanding:

Levels of Understanding

▼ **The child records the number of candies in a haphazard way. It is impossible to decipher the data at a later time.**

▼ **The child records the number of candies randomly. It is difficult to determine the number of candies for each color, but not impossible.**

▼ **The child organizes the data about the number and color of candies effectively. The results are organized and easy to interpret.**

Donna makes neat columns for her candy, yet did not use color codes or labels. Thus, her data is impossible to decipher, and she is at the first level of understanding.

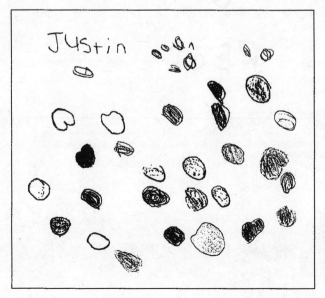

Justin is at the second level of understanding. He uses different color crayons to match the colors of the candy and records them in a random fashion on his paper.

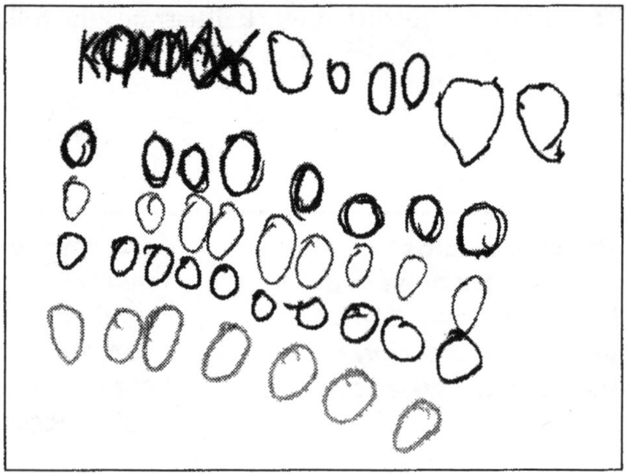

Kimmy is at the highest level of understanding. She organized her report in rows according to the color of the candy.

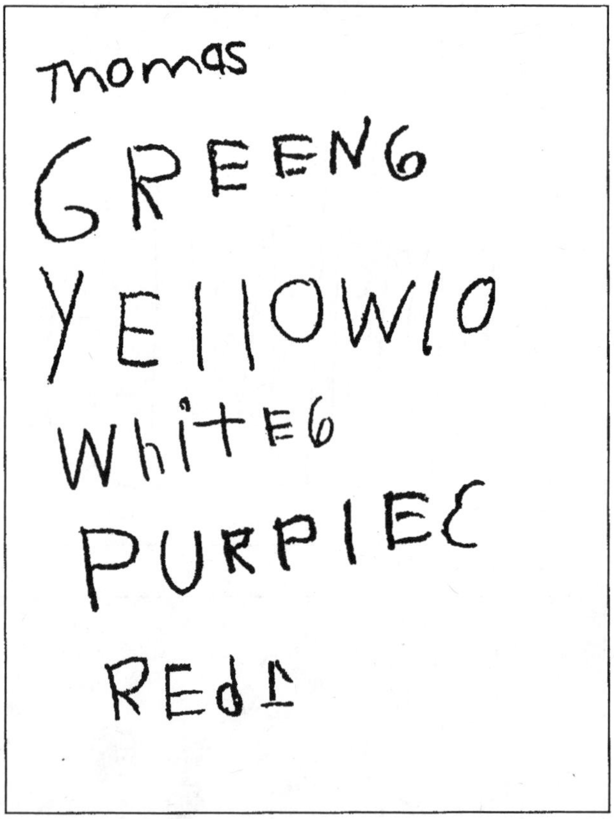

Thomas

GREEN6

YELLOW10

WHITE6

PURPLE C

RED L

Thomas is also at this level. He creates a list of each color candy and the number he found of each color.

These children are placed as follows on the levels of understanding:

Levels of Understanding

Donna	Justin	Kimmy Thomas
▼	▼	▼
The child records the number of candies haphazard way. It is impossible to decipher the data at a later time.	The child records the number of candies randomly. It is difficult to determine the number of candies for each color, but not impossible.	The child organizes the data about the number and color of candies effectively. The results are organized and easy to interpret.

A first and second grade classroom also generated their own ideas for using the M & M's for math problems. They brainstormed a list that was similar to the kindergarten list and then explored some of their own ideas. Here is the list they generated:

Things to Do With M & M's

- See how many of each color
- Make shapes out of them
- Put in groups of twos and threes
- Subtract with them
- Put in a line and eat by colors
- Add with them
- See if every bag has the same number

The children wanted to closely follow the activities from the book first, so the teacher decided that her class could explore the activities with the M & M's on one day and then write the results more formally the next day. Before the children began writing on the second day, they were all puzzled about why each bag had a different number of candies in it. After they discussed possible reasons for the differences in the total numbers, the teacher charted their ideas and posted them in the classroom.

In this first and second grade class, the children's reports can be grouped on the following levels of understanding:

Levels of Understanding

▼	▼	▼
The child presents a basic description of one or more of the activities, and uses few or no mathematical terms to describe them.	The child presents a partial description of two or more activities and uses some mathematical terms to describe them.	The child presents a complete description of all the activities and consistently uses mathematical terms to describe them.

M & m's

Richie

What we did we put
them in shase. we did
M & m's math. and it
wus fun. I like it.
they are moñ.

Richie is at the first level of understanding. He describes one of the activities — putting the M & M's in shapes — and stated it was fun. [There is no reference to the discrepancy in totals.]

Andrew

I have 23
M&Ms
There are
5 Yellow
5 red   We
4 tan   tok Them
               opo+r
6 brown   And Sdrtd
1 gree   Them
2 orange

Andrew is at the second level of understanding because he writes about sorting and counting the individual M & M's by colors and states the total (but does not compare his total to the number of candies in other bags.)

Both Christel and Megan are at the highest level of understanding as they report their experiences with the M & M's.

Christel

See how many of each color there is.
Make shapes out of them.
Put in groups of 2's, 3's.
Subtract with them.

Put in a line and eat by colors.

Put in Group by colors.
Then we made square,
then a circle, then a triangle.
there were diffrent amouts in each
bag and that was not fair to the
whole class. And there were not enough
red's because there were not enough red's
in each bag. The math we did was
Subtracting and Adding with them
and how we subtracted by eating them.

Christel tells about each activity she did and then talks about the different amounts in each package and the unfairness of this.

Megan   m & m
The first step was.

See how many of each color there
is. We put them in groups of colors.
We made shaps out of them. Then
We put them in groups of 2, 3; Then we
suptract them. Then we put them in a
tine and aet by colors. Then we did math
we added and sudtract them. Some bags had
27 m&m in them. They put m&m in by
weat.

Megan also carefully describes the activities and explains that the candy company put the M & M's in by weight.

The work of these first and second grade children may be placed on the levels of understanding as follows:

Levels of Understanding

Richie ▼	Andrew ▼	Christel Megan ▼
The child presents a basic description of one or more of the activities, and uses few or no mathematical terms to describe them.	The child presents a partial description of two or more activities and uses some mathematical terms to describe them.	The child presents a complete description of all the activities and consistently uses mathematical terms to describe them.

In all three classrooms described, the children decided the mathematical questions they wanted to pose. The teacher charted the ideas and became a facilitator as the children sought the answers to their own questions. Many teachers reported that they were surprised by how much the children learned from the activities they suggested, planned and implemented. For example, the children who constructed the rainbows applied the concept of *more* or *less* and also worked with the idea of parallel arcs as they constructed their rainbows. In pairs, these kindergarten children came to their own conclusions that they needed to place the most frequent color of the candy on the outside layer of the arc, and then put the remaining colors on the inside of the arc, in descending order.

Because of the variety of problems explored by the children in each class, each teacher used different levels of understanding to look at the children's work. They found that the best way to create their own levels of understanding was to look for trends as they read through the written work. The next step was to divide the work into appropriate piles and identify the common attributes of each of the piles. All three of the teachers, however, felt that the notes they took as the children solved the problems were even more important than the written

records the children created. They were excited to try this activity again to see growth over time in the children's ability to think mathematically, solve problems effectively, and communicate their findings.

This problem is one that the children can revisit over and over again throughout the school year. By changing the "sweet treats" used, the investigation takes on a new "flavor" each time it is presented to the children.

References

Barbieri McGrath, Barbara. *The M&M's Counting Book*. Waterton, MA: Charlesbridge Publishing, 2002.

A Closer Look at Student Work

This book is meant to be a starting point for teachers who wish to explore open-ended problems with their children. Some lessons pose teacher-directed questions, such as **Eggs and Chicks** and **How Many Snails?** Other lessons allow the children to formulate and answer their own questions, as in **Sweet Treats**. Many of the lessons contain suggestions for revisiting the same type of problem throughout the year.

Whether the open-ended question is teacher-directed or child-generated, keep in mind these three important considerations:

1 **It is essential to have students explain their written work so that you can gain a fuller understanding of each child's mathematical thinking. In addition, sharing of written work helps children consider other viewpoints and appreciate divergent approaches to problem-solving.** Often the child's ability to explain things in writing lags behind his or her ability to solve the problem. Young children often have a limited ability to communicate with paper and pencil. In order to explain their ideas completely, sharing with the teacher and the class is a vital part of their communication and lends additional support to their writing.

2 **Revisit lessons throughout the year to encourage revision and document growth over time.** The lessons in this book need to be repeated in their original or modified form to insure optimum student performance, to provide an accurate picture of what the children are learning, and to strengthen their ability to solve problems and communicate mathematically.

3 **Recognize that children need support and encouragement to risk and grow mathematically.** Children will not prosper in mathematics if they learn that the teacher knows the correct answer and best approach to every mathematics problem. In an open-ended setting, teachers must step back and trust that the children will arrive at a developmentally appropriate answer in their own manner. Often, the solution will not be immediately accessible to the children, and they will need to learn from their mistakes without fear of failure and listen to the wisdom of their classmates. It takes time, trust and patience on the part of the teacher and child to set up an environment that is conducive to open-ended problem-solving.

This chapter will provide examples from the classroom will illustrate these considerations and the benefits both children and teachers will receive as they explore open-ended problems in mathematics.

Share Written Work

As she approached the wheels problem (see page 30), Mayra, a second grader, drew a picture of the modes of transportation and her written work depicted the following solution, as shown to the left.

At first glance, the equation $5 + 2 + 2 = 24$ appears to indicate that Mayra had made some computation errors. Yet, she arrived at a correct answer. Because her written explanation is limited, her teacher was able to gain more information when she asked Mayra to explain the equation. Mayra replied that the 5 in the number sentence meant there were five cars with four wheels each and that made twenty wheels. The two 2's represented the wheels on the bicycles. When she was given the opportunity to clarify her answer, Mayra was able to explain how the equation represented her answer of 24 wheels. Thus, her teachers and her classmates had a clearer picture of her mathematical thinking.

In another classroom, Ricky shared his work with blocks. He showed his picture and read the sentence, "I used triangles and a 'longangle.'" The children listened intently until he finished. A child in the class then suggested he use the word "rectangle," instead of longangle. Ricky took the suggestion and revised his report to include the new word. If he had not shared his written work, he would not have made that adjustment.

Revisit Problems to Encourage Revision and Document Growth Over Time

You will gain evidence of growth in mathematical thinking over time if children revisit the same problem or adaptations of that problem. For example, young children need many opportunities with data collection to discover effective ways to represent data and make logical conclusions based on their findings. It is important for children to explore and share their ideas in a non-threatening atmosphere that encourages discussion and revision of student work. If you revisit activities at a later date, children have the opportunity to apply and build on prior knowledge and develop new approaches in new but similar situations.

For example, the Safari Toss activity (page 51) requires children to use an animal die to collect data. On this die, three sides have a picture of a turtle, two sides have pictures of a giraffe, and one side has a picture of an elephant. Other die patterns are included so the children can revisit this activity several times during the school year. For December, the holiday die has three sides with bells, two with candles, and one with a dreidel. In March, the die has four sides with a shamrock and two with a pot of gold.

In November, the children in one first and second grade class used the animal dice activity to gather and analyze data. When the activity was complete, the class compared methods for recording the data. They also talked briefly about the methods of recording that would be easiest to read and most efficient. The children's work was put in portfolios for later use.

The next month, the teacher cut and pasted holiday pictures to change the die. The children were again asked to roll the die thirty or more times and record the data. On the following day, the children used their data recording sheets to report about their findings. Again the class discussed the various methods for recording, looking for clear and efficient ways of make note of each roll of the die.

Finally in March, the children repeated the activity with the St. Patrick's Day die that was described previously. The class again discussed the finished work in relation to clarity and efficiency of the responses.

In each of the three times that children explored the dice activities, the teacher resisted the urge to tell the children how to record the data. They worked either alone or with a partner and without adult intervention while their teacher circulated about the room observing them complete the task. She was interested in finding out if the previous discussion times had an influence over how they collected the data.

Hoping to see growth in the way the children approached the task of data collection, the teacher compared the students' work from the initial and subsequent dice activities. She was encouraged to see that most children found a more efficient way of recording with each successive lesson. Kali and Aimee's work (as shown on the next 2 pages) both illustrate this growth.

Kali, for instance, carefully drew each animal each time she recorded the first time in November. It was difficult to tell at a glance the total number of rolls for each animal. In December, she became more efficient by numbering her rolls in specific columns. In March, Kali used tally counting, circled the groups of ten, wrote the totals and included a detailed written report to interpret the data.

Kali, November

dradle	Candle	bell
12345	1234567	1234567
6789	8910 11 12	8910 11 12
10 11 12	13 14 15 16	13 14 15 16 17
13 14 15	17 18 19 20	18 19 20 21
16 17 18	21 22 23	22 23 24
19 20	24 25 26	25 26 27 28
21 22	27 28 29	29 30 31 32
23	30 31 32	33 34 35 36
	33 34	
	35 36 37	
	38 39 40	
	41 42	

Kali, December

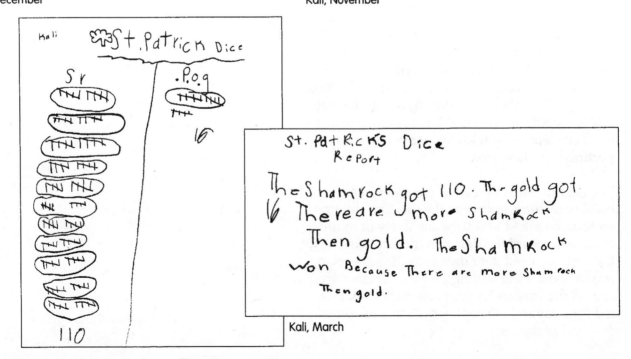

Kali, March

For the Safari Toss (November), Aimee wrote an entire sentence to record each roll of the animal dice. This was a less efficient procedure than the slash marks she made to record the Holiday Dice in December. She commented that it took her a long time to count the individual marks and she kept losing her place. When Kali shared her numbering system, she raised her hand and said, "That's what I should have done." With the St. Patrick's Day die in March she did exactly that — she used Kali's numbering system.

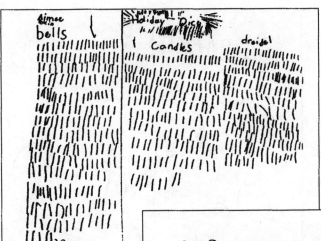

Aimee, November

Aimee, December

Aimee, March

Through class discussion and sharing of data collection methods, the children learn new ways to record data. By revisiting this problem throughout the year, the children were able to grow by listening to and discussing ideas with the class. This discourse, coupled with time to assimilate the new concepts, allows children to grow mathematically in a natural, supportive and positive manner.

Provide Support and Encouragement

In order to risk and grow mathematically, children need our support and encouragement. This means that we must trust that every child is going to become more mathematically powerful if we provide the proper climate for that growth. The child needs the opportunity to struggle with concepts and the chance to revise or change answers as new knowledge is embraced.

Sammy is a child whose growth in mathematics is quite dramatic. With support and encouragement, he became an effective problem-solver.

At the beginning of the school year, Sammy tried to make sense out of the Eggs and Chicks problem by drawing chicks and eggs. He was unable to relate his drawing to the mathematics in the problem. Although Sammy was at the most basic level of understanding, his teacher did not say that he failed to solve the problem. Instead, she exposed him to more successful models of other solutions.

A few days later, Sammy tackled the wheels problem. He placed the correct number of children in the proper vehicles — two on bikes and five in the van. The number of wheels he pictured is not accurate. When the teacher asked him about the number of wheels, he counted them and said, "Eleven." Again, he was given time and support to further develop his thinking.

Sammy

M & M Colors

Six Yellows Six brown

three tals five green sever
three red

Orange

As the year progressed, Sammy's ability to respond to the problems grew as he watched the other children and listened to their responses. He became clearer and more organized in his approach to mathematical problem-solving.

At the end of October, Sammy sorted his M & M's into colors and efficiently reported the color and number of each candy.

Sammy   Animal Dice

1 giraffe

2 turtle

3 giraffe

4 turtle

5 elephant

6 turtle

7 giraffe

8 elephant

9 turtle

10 giraffe

11 giraffe

12 turtle

13 turtle

14 turtle giraffe

15 elephant

16 elephant

17 turtle

18 elephant

19 giraffe

In November, Sammy listed each of the names of the animals in order as he rolled the animal dice.

Throughout the year, Sammy developed more sophistication in his ability to communicate mathematically.

In March, he explored another dice problem, and this time tried something modeled by one of his class-mates in a prior dice lesson. Al-though it is not easy to determine the total number of rolls for each die, Sammy organized his data into columns and you can tell at a glance which outcome occurred most frequently.

Later in the spring, Sammy re-sponded to the duckling problem with a charming story. After the 3 ducklings wander off, they soon return. His response also indicates increased confidence in his ability to construct mathematical conclu-sions.

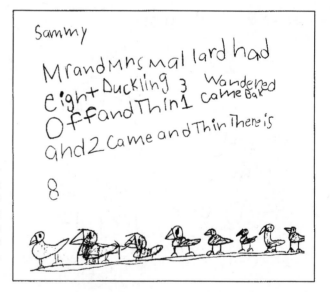

The environment in Sammy's classroom was conducive to encouraging mathematical growth. First, Sammy's teacher realized that his response to the Eggs and Chicks problem was a typical response of a first grade child that has seldom been asked these kinds of questions. She trusted that Sammy would progress, given the time and opportunity to experience several more problems. She did not expect, at the beginning of school, that every child would be able to easily solve this problem. In fact, throughout the year, she knew that children would be on different levels in various areas of mathematics.

Next, Sammy's teacher did not use the levels of understanding to limit Sammy's potential as a problem solver. The levels of understanding shown in this book are merely a range of how children might typically respond to these questions. She did, however, look for ways to help Sammy more fully understand the next questions, and celebrated his progress.

And finally, Sammy was able to learn from his peers through discussion and sharing of work. Sammy's classroom is a collaborative one in which the children freely share ideas and thoughts about mathematics. The children know that mistakes are opportunities for learning, and that it may take several days to complete one problem. Sammy recognizes that the search for the answer, including wrong answers, are a vital part of the learning process.

As we review Sammy's work over a year's time, we gain a perspective of how we want children to progress. Without a focus on what he did "wrong," and with an emphasis on his strengths, Sammy was able to make considerable growth in his mathematical power by the end of the year.

Keep these ideas in mind as you explore and extend the activities from this book to embark on an open-ended problem solving journey with the children in your classroom.

Bibliography

Author Unknown, *Mix & Match Educational Book Set*, Atlanta, GA: Dalmatian Press.

Baratta-Lorton, Mary. *Mathematics Their Way*. Menlo Park, CA: Addison-Wesley, 1976.

Baratta-Lorton, Mary. *Workjobs II*. Menlo Park, CA: Addison-Wesley, 1979.

Barbieri McGrath, Barbara. *The M&M's Counting Book*. Waterton, MA: Charlesbridge Publishing, 2002.

Baylor, Byrd. *Everybody Needs a Rock*. New York: Aladdin Paperbacks, 1985.

Bogart, Jo Ellen. *10 for Dinner*. New York: Scholastic Inc., 1989.

Brett, Jan. *The Mitten*. New York: Putnam Juvenile; Boardbook edition, 2002.

Burton, Virginia Lee. *Choo Choo*. New York: Houghton Mifflin Harcourt, 1988.

Butler, M. Christine. *Too Many Eggs*. Boston: David R. Godine, 1988.

Crews, Donald. *Freight Train*. New York: Greenwillow Books, 1992.

Fox, Mem. *Radical Reflections*. New York: Houghton Mifflin Harcourt, 2001.

Garland, Cynthia. *Mathematics Their Way Summary Newsletter*, Saratoga, CA: Center for Innovation in Education, 1990.

Giganti, Paul. *How Many Snails?* New York: Greenwillow Books, 1994.

Hoban, Russell. *A Bargain for Frances*. New York: HarperCollins Childrens Books, 1992.

Hoban, Tana. *Is It Rough? Is It Smooth? Is It Shiny?* New York: Greenwillow Books, 1984.

Hoban, Tana. *Shapes, Shapes, Shapes*. New York: HarperCollins Publishers, 1996.

Kahalewai, Marilyn. *Whose Slippers Are Those?* Honolulu: The Bess Press, 2005.

Linehan, Anne. *Stretch It! Creative Geoboard Tasks for Developing Mathematical Teaching*. San Leandro, CA: Watten/Poe Teaching Resource Center, 1992.

McCloskey, Robert. *Make Way for Ducklings*. New York: Puffin; Pap/Com Ed., 2010.

Miller, Margaret. *Whose Shoes?* New York: HarperCollins Publishers, 1991.

Min, Laura. Mrs. *Sato's Hens*. St. Paul, MN: Globe Publishing, 2000.

Moerbeek, Kees. *All Mixed Up*. Los Angeles: Price Stern Sloan, 1994.

Moerbeek, Kees. *Boo Whoo?* Los Angeles: Price Stern Sloan, 1993.

Moerbeek, Kees. *New at the Zoo 2*. New York: Random House, 1993.

Morris, Ann. *Hats, Hats, Hats*. New York: HarperCollins Publishers, 1993.

National Council of Teachers of Mathematics (NCTM). *Curriculum and Evaluation Standards for School Mathematics*. Reston, VA: NCTM, 1989.

Piper, Watty. *The Little Engine That Could*. New York: Grosset & Dunlap, 1991.

Reid, Margarette S. *The Button Box*. New York: Penguin Group USA, 1995.

Russo, Marisabina. *The Line Up Book*. New York: Greenwillow Books, 1986.

Steig, William. *Sylvester and the Magic Pebble*. New York: Aladdin Paperbacks, 1987.

Tresselt, Alvin. *The Mitten*. New York: HarperCollins Publishers, 1989.

Math Perspectives
Teacher Development Center

Math Perspectives publishes professional resources and provides long-term professional development and courses for teachers of K-5 mathematics.

Learn more about our wide range of professional development institutes, courses, and long-term professional development.

Visit mathperspectives.com or call 360-715-2782.

MATH PERSPECTIVES Book and Resources Resources
Kathy Richardson, Author

How Chilren Learn Number Concepts:
A Guide to the Critical Learning Phases

Assessing Math Concepts Series
- *Counting Objects*
- *Changing Numbers*
- *More/Less Trains*
- *Number Arrangements*
- *Combination Trains*
- *Hiding Assessments*
- *Ten Frames*
- *Grouping Tens*
- *Two-Digit Addition and Subtraction*

Understanding Numbers Series
- *Place Value*
- *Addition and Subtraction*
- *Decimals*

Developing Math Concepts in Pre-Kindergarten

Math Time: The Learning Environment

Professional Development DVDs
- *The Learning Environment for K-2 Mathematics:*
  What Does It Look Like?
- *Thinking With Numbers: Number Talks*
- *Making it Work in the Classroom*
- *A Look at Children's Thinking*